The **Basic Skills** Agency

fresh start
in the workplace

Getting the basics right in
Construction
(Common Occupations)
– Trowel Occupations
– Wood Occupations
– Plastering

Mapping the Adult Literacy and Numeracy Standards
to the occupational standards of the
Construction Industry Training Board

BP

CITB

Published July 2001

ISBN 1 85990 165 4

Design: Studio 21

Contents

1. Introduction

By basic skills we mean:

> *the ability to read, write and speak in English and to use mathematics at a level necessary to function and progress at work and in society in general.*

The Government's National Strategy for basic skills has identified clear targets for improving levels of literacy and numeracy amongst the general population. Research has shown that almost one in four adults has difficulties with literacy and even greater numbers need help with numeracy.

> *People at work need good basic skills not just because of the needs of a particular job. Such abilities are essential to perform a wide range of activities safely and effectively within the workplace.*
>
> Improving literacy and numeracy – A fresh start (DfEE, 1999)

Many of the adults with poor literacy and numeracy skills are in the workplace or are undergoing occupational training. The national strategy for improving adult literacy and numeracy skills makes clear the important contribution that can be made by National Training Organisations.

> *NTOs have a key role, and literacy and numeracy skills should be a key feature of their workforce development plans.*
>
> Skills for Life (DfEE, 2001)

The Basic Skills Agency has been working closely with NTOs to map their occupational standards to the *National Standards for Adult Literacy and Adult Numeracy*. These maps are intended for use in training and development for all staff within the sector.

We have worked closely with each National Training Organisation to ensure that the basic skills standards in these maps reflect the range of skills and knowledge required by workers to perform the occupational tasks.

The occupational standards, have been mapped to the *National Standards for Adult Literacy and Adult Numeracy* at the appropriate level; either Entry 3, Level 1 or Level 2. Careful account has been taken of the basic skills demands of jobs and the National Training Organisation has contributed to this process by providing examples of work instructions, health and safety guidelines and other materials in use in the workplace and in training. The National Training Organisation has also been fully involved in the process of review and evaluation of these maps at each stage.

The identification and selection of Units to be included in this document has been carried out by the NTO. The Core or Mandatory Units and Optional Units for the NVQs derived from these occupational standards are indicated on the back cover of this document. In some cases, all the necessary Units for the NVQ will be included, in others the NTO will have prioritised the most popular Units for inclusion.

		Key Skills Level 5	National qualifications framework Level 5
		Key Skills Level 4	National qualifications framework Level 4
		Key Skills Level 3	National qualifications framework Level 3
	Literacy/Numeracy Level 2	Key Skills Level 2	National qualifications framework Level 2
National Curriculum Level 5	Literacy/Numeracy Level 1	Key Skills Level 1	National qualifications framework Level 1
National Curriculum Level 4			
National Curriculum Level 3	Literacy/Numeracy Entry 3		
National Curriculum Level 2	Literacy/Numeracy Entry 2		Entry Level
National Curriculum Level 1	Literacy/Numeracy Entry 1		

2. Workplace basic skills

How many employees have difficulties with basic skills?

23% of people of working age have low levels of literacy and numeracy – almost 7 million people.

Fact

All countries have problems with poor literacy and numeracy, but the UK, when compared with other developed nations, has more problems than most – 23% with very low literacy skills in the UK, compared with 7% in Sweden and 12% in Germany.

Source: Adult Literacy in Britain, ONS

What does this mean in real numbers of employees?

Population of England	49.3 million
61.4% of working age (16-59/64)	30.27 million
23% of people of working age are likely to have 'very poor' basic skills	6.96 million

Source: Adult Literacy in Britain, ONS

It is a fact that in small and medium sized businesses, over 2 million workers are likely to have poor basic skills. In large organisations a further 2 million employees have difficulties with basic skills and in the public sector there are a million more workers with poor basic skills.

What are the consequences of poor basic skills amongst employees?

Workers with poor basic skills are at a considerable disadvantage in the workplace. Research has shown that employees with basic skills difficulties:

- will be less likely to receive work-related training;
- will have a limited number of jobs open to them;
- may find themselves vulnerable in times of change;
- often turn down promotion because they are afraid of the paperwork;
- will often be in lower paid jobs.

What are the consequences for employers?

Many of the problems experienced at work are linked to poor basic skills. Training, health and safety, quality procedures and many more issues are affected by employees who lack the skills to deal with the requirements of the workplace. Poor basic skills may mean:

- poor productivity;
- administration errors with customer orders;
- increased wastage rates;
- poor customer relations;

- incorrect production of orders;

- increased machine downtime;

- inefficiency of production or provision of services;

- increased staff turnover;

- difficulties over the introduction of new methods of working and new technology;

- external recruitment instead of internal promotion.

And what about the economy?

The Moser Report, *Improving literacy and numeracy – A fresh start,* published in 1999, suggested that poor basic skills might be one of the reasons for low productivity in the UK economy.

> ‘At work, basic skills matter crucially. They are a key to employability … And there is evidence that they are growing in importance, employers rate them ever more highly. Moreover, poor basic skills affect the efficiency and competitiveness of the economy. The pace of development and change in business is undermined. They represent a significant cost to British industry. ’

A report, quoted by David Blunkett in 1997, suggested that poor literacy costs business and government £10 billion every year.

Source: *Education and Training and their Impact on the Economy,* Ernst and Young

What are the benefits of providing training and improving the levels of basic skills amongst workers?

- Ability to improve performance and meet targets

- Increased efficiency and productivity

- Improved staff retention and commitment

- Improved staff take-up and benefit from training

- Ability to re-deploy staff

- Improved customer service

- Improved skills and confidence amongst workers

- Increased ability to perform jobs to national standards and achieve accreditation

3. Mapping rationale

How many Adult Literacy and Numeracy Standards are shown for each occupational standard of work?

The mapping has been carried out using a number of factors in order to decide the appropriate choice of Adult Literacy and Numeracy Standards. In collaboration with the NTO, we have decided on the **main**, or **critical**, basic skills required in order to perform each of the performance criteria or work standards.

In some cases, there will be only one Adult Literacy and Numeracy Standard mapped, for example, *Reading* in order to follow straightforward work instructions. For other performance criteria, more than one Adult Literacy and Numeracy Standard will be included in the map, for example, *Speaking and listening* and *Writing* will be shown when a worker has to make a report both verbally and in writing.

Which Adult Literacy and Numeracy Standard statements have been used and why?

As a general rule, in these maps the main purpose of the work standard has been the guiding factor in deciding which of the following basic skills statements is used.

Speaking and Listening

- *Speak to communicate* – if the main purpose of the task is to give information.
- *Listen and respond* – if the main purpose is to receive or gain information.
- *Engage in discussion* – in cases where there is a requirement to engage in an exchange of information.

Reading

- *Read and understand* – in instances when the worker needs to read a range of texts in order to gain understanding about concepts or principles.
- *Read and obtain information* – when the worker needs to follow a set of guidelines or written instructions in order to complete a task or procedure.

Writing

- *Write to communicate* – this statement covers all the occasions when a worker would need to write in order to perform a task. The appropriate descriptor would then apply eg information, ideas or opinions, depending on the context.

Numeracy

- *Understanding and using mathematical information* – this statement has generally been used to describe tasks where information, problems or instructions are given in numerical form (a product specification, product codes, charts and timetables).
- *Calculating and manipulating mathematical information* – is used when actual calculations have to be done and results are generated (calibrating a machine, weighing items, handling money).
- *Interpreting results and communicating mathematical information* – this is used when a task involves reporting or recording mathematical information (stock control sheets, quality data sheets).

Which level has been chosen and why?

Three levels from the Standards have been used in these maps.

- *Entry 3* – this level includes work tasks involving text, writing and numeracy in familiar and everyday contexts and of limited length.

- *Level 1* – this level has been chosen to describe the skills required to perform routine and straightforward work tasks of varying length.

- *Level 2* – this is used where tasks at work are more complex or non-routine.

4. Guidelines for use

How to use the grids

The basic skills grids provide an 'at-a-glance' overview of the range and levels of basic skills required for each unit. From this section you can move to the detailed information about basic skills in the maps, for the purposes of training or staff development. The diagram below illustrates how to use the grids.

Basic Skills Grid

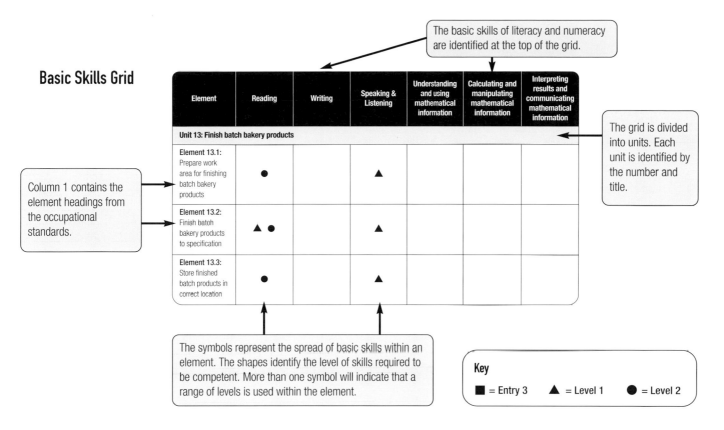

The basic skills of literacy and numeracy are identified at the top of the grid.

The grid is divided into units. Each unit is identified by the number and title.

Column 1 contains the element headings from the occupational standards.

The symbols represent the spread of basic skills within an element. The shapes identify the level of skills required to be competent. More than one symbol will indicate that a range of levels is used within the element.

Key
■ = Entry 3   ▲ = Level 1   ● = Level 2

How to use the maps

The maps are presented at Element level with all the national standards of work mapped to the required Adult Literacy and Numeracy Standards at the appropriate level. The diagram below illustrates how to use the map to identify the skills and levels of reading, writing, speaking and listening and number that underpin the occupational standards.

Basic Skills Map

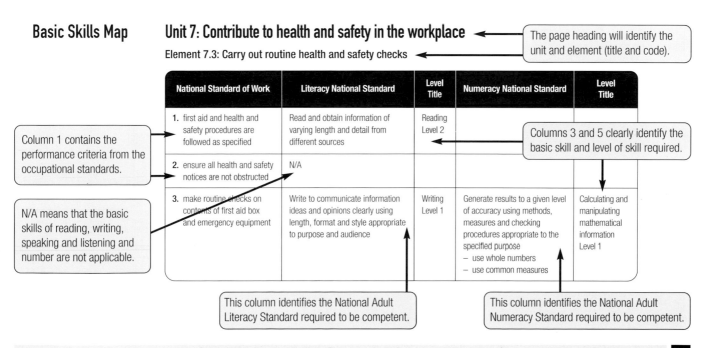

The page heading will identify the unit and element (title and code).

Column 1 contains the performance criteria from the occupational standards.

N/A means that the basic skills of reading, writing, speaking and listening and number are not applicable.

Columns 3 and 5 clearly identify the basic skill and level of skill required.

This column identifies the National Adult Literacy Standard required to be competent.

This column identifies the National Adult Numeracy Standard required to be competent.

Progression from the Adult Literacy and Numeracy Standards to the Adult Literacy and Numeracy Core Curriculum

In Sections 7 and 8 of this document you will find:

- an overview of the Adult Literacy and Numeracy Standards used in the maps;
- progression tables in speaking and listening, reading and writing, number, measures, shape and space and handling data.

The progression tables include:

- all the curriculum elements demonstrating the skills and knowledge required for teaching and learning;
- the curriculum references that lead you directly to the required part of the Adult Literacy and Numeracy Core Curriculum documents.

This diagram illustrates how the progression works.

Element 9.1: Process valid passenger tickets and passes

National Standard of Work	Literacy National Standard	Level Title	Numeracy National Standard	Level Title
1. confirm that the equipment used for processing tickets is in approved operational condition	N/A			
2. explain details of fares clearly to passengers in a manner that promotes understanding and goodwill	Speak to communicate information adapting speech and content to take account of the listener(s) and the medium	Speaking and Listening Level 1		
3. process fares in accordance . . .	Read and obtain information . . .	Reading Level 1	Generate results to a given level of accuracy . . .	

Actual page from curriculum

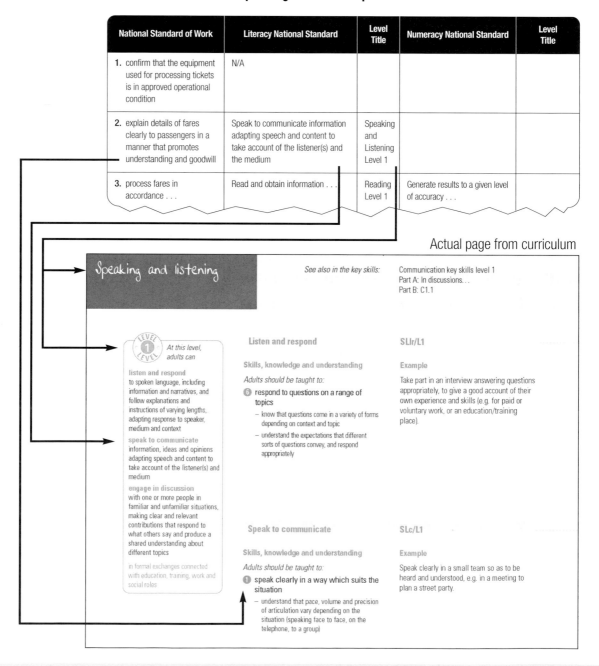

Speaking and listening

See also in the key skills:
Communication key skills level 1
Part A: In discussions...
Part B: C1.1

LEVEL 1 *At this level, adults can*

listen and respond
to spoken language, including information and narratives, and follow explanations and instructions of varying lengths, adapting response to speaker, medium and context

speak to communicate
information, ideas and opinions adapting speech and content to take account of the listener(s) and medium

engage in discussion
with one or more people in familiar and unfamiliar situations, making clear and relevant contributions that respond to what others say and produce a shared understanding about different topics

in formal exchanges connected with education, training, work and social roles

Listen and respond

Skills, knowledge and understanding
Adults should be taught to:
6 respond to questions on a range of topics
   – know that questions come in a variety of forms depending on context and topic
   – understand the expectations that different sorts of questions convey, and respond appropriately

Speak to communicate

Skills, knowledge and understanding
Adults should be taught to:
1 speak clearly in a way which suits the situation
   – understand that pace, volume and precision of articulation vary depending on the situation (speaking face to face, on the telephone, to a group)

SLlr/L1

Example

Take part in an interview answering questions appropriately, to give a good account of their own experience and skills (e.g. for paid or voluntary work, or an education/training place).

SLc/L1

Example

Speak clearly in a small team so as to be heard and understood, e.g. in a meeting to plan a street party.

5. Basic Skills Grids — Trowel Occupations

an overview of each Unit

Trowel Occupations

Element	Reading	Writing	Speaking & Listening	Understanding and using mathematical information	Calculating and manipulating mathematical information	Interpreting results and communicating mathematical information
Unit MR 01: Load and Unload resources						
Element MR01.1: Select resources	▲		▲		▲	
Element MR01.2: Move resources manually	▲ ●		▲			
Element MR01.3: Comply with safe working practices	▲ ●		▲			
Unit MR 02: Contribute to erecting and dismantling working platforms						
Element MR02.1: Select resources	▲		▲		▲	
Element MR02.2: Assist with erecting and dismantling access equipment	▲ ●		▲			
Element MR02.3: Comply with safe working practices	▲ ●		▲			
Unit MR 03: Contribute to maintaining work relationships						
Element MR03.1: Identify potential areas of conflict			●			
Element MR03.2: Maintain relationships with colleagues			●			
Unit 180: Prepare and mix materials						
Element MR180.1: Select materials	▲		▲		▲	
Element MR180.2: Mix materials	▲ ●		▲		▲	
Element MR180.3: Comply with safe working practices	▲ ●		▲			

Trowel Occupations

Element	Reading	Writing	Speaking & Listening	Understanding and using mathematical information	Calculating and manipulating mathematical information	Interpreting results and communicating mathematical information
Unit 181: Prepare components						
Element MR181.1: Select components	▲		▲		▲	
Element MR181.2: Mark out and cut components	▲ ●		▲			
Element MR181.3: Comply with safe working practices	▲ ●		▲			
Unit 182: Position components to line						
Element MR182.1: Select materials and components	▲		▲		▲	
Element MR182.2: Position components	▲ ●		▲		▲	
Element MR182.3: Comply with safe working practices	▲ ●		▲			
Unit 183: Contribute to setting out positions						
Element MR183.1: Select resources	▲		▲		▲	
Element MR183.2: Contribute to setting out work	▲ ●		▲		▲	
Element MR183.3: Comply with safe working practices	▲ ●		▲			
Unit 184: Contribute to laying concrete						
Element MR184.1: Select resources	▲		▲		▲	
Element MR184.2: Contribute to concreting work	▲ ●		▲			
Element MR184.3: Comply with safe working practices	▲ ●		▲			

Trowel Occupations

Element	Reading	Writing	Speaking & Listening	Understanding and using mathematical information	Calculating and manipulating mathematical information	Interpreting results and communicating mathematical information
Unit 185: Contribute to forming surface finishes						
Element MR185.1: Select resources	▲		▲		▲	
Element MR185.2: form surface finishes to materials	▲ ●		▲			
Element MR185.3: Comply with safe working practices	▲ ●		▲			
Unit PR 07: Carry out slinging and signalling for the movement of loads						
Element 1: Prepare and sling loads for lifting	▲		▲ ●			
Element 2: Direct and control the movement and placing of loads	▲ ●		▲			

Getting the basics right in Construction (Common Occupations)

Basic Skills Grids – Wood Occupations

an overview of each Unit

Wood Occupations

Element	Reading	Writing	Speaking & Listening	Understanding and using mathematical information	Calculating and manipulating mathematical information	Interpreting results and communicating mathematical information
Unit MR 01: Load and Unload resources						
Element MR01.1: Select resources	▲		▲		▲	
Element MR01.2: Move resources manually	▲ ●		▲			
Element MR01.3: Comply with safe working practices	▲ ●		▲			
Unit MR 02: Contribute to erecting and dismantling working platforms						
Element MR02.1: Select resources	▲		▲		▲	
Element MR02.2: Assist with erecting and dismantling access equipment	▲ ●		▲			
Element MR02.3: Comply with safe working practices	▲ ●		▲			
Unit MR 03: Contribute to maintaining work relationships						
Element MR03.1: Identify potential areas of conflict			●			
Element MR03.2: Maintain relationships with colleagues			●			
Unit MR 05: Set up and use portable power tools						
Element MR05.1: Select resources	▲		▲		▲	
Element MR05.2: Operate power tools	▲ ●		▲		▲	
Element MR05.3: Comply with safe working practices	▲ ●		▲			

Getting the basics right in Construction (Common Occupations)

Wood Occupations

Element	Reading	Writing	Speaking & Listening	Understanding and using mathematical information	Calculating and manipulating mathematical information	Interpreting results and communicating mathematical information
Unit MR 138: Maintain and use woodworking hand tools						
Element MR138.1: Select resources	▲		▲		▲	
Element MR138.2: Work materials using hand tools	▲ ●		▲			
Element MR138.3: Comply with safe working practices	▲ ●		▲			
Unit MR 139: Form basio woodworking joints						
Element MR139.1: Select resources	▲		▲		▲	
Element MR139.2: Mark out and form joints	▲ ●		▲	▲	▲	
Element MR139.3: Comply with safe working practices	▲ ●		▲			
Unit MR 140: Install components hung on hinges						
Element MR140.1: Select resources	▲		▲		▲	
Element MR140.2: Hang hinged components	▲ ●		▲			
Element MR140.3: Comply with safe working practices	▲ ●		▲			
Unit MR 141: Install door ironmongery components						
Element MR141.1: Select resources	▲		▲		▲	
Element MR142.2: Fit ironmongery	▲ ●		▲	▲		
Element MR143.3: Comply with safe working practices	▲ ●		▲			

Wood Occupations

Key
■ = Entry 3   ▲ = Level 1   ● = Level 2

Element	Reading	Writing	Speaking & Listening	Understanding and using mathematical information	Calculating and manipulating mathematical information	Interpreting results and communicating mathematical information
Unit MR 142: Install internal mouldings						
Element MR142.1: Select resources	▲		▲		▲	
Element MR142.2: Position and secure mouldings	▲ ●		▲			
Element MR142.3: Comply with safe working practices	▲ ●		▲			

Basic Skills Grids – Plastering

an overview of each Unit

Plastering

Element	Reading	Writing	Speaking & Listening	Understanding and using mathematical information	Calculating and manipulating mathematical information	Interpreting results and communicating mathematical information
Unit MR 01: Load and Unload resources						
Element 1: Select resources	▲		▲		▲	
Element 2: Move resources manually	▲ ●		▲			
Element 3: Comply with safe working practices	▲ ●		▲			
Unit MR 02: Contribute to erecting and dismantling working platforms						
Element 1: Select resources	▲		▲		▲	
Element 2: Assist with erecting and dismantling access equipment	▲ ●		▲			
Element 3: Comply with safe working practices	▲ ●		▲			
Unit MR 03: Contribute to maintaining work relationships						
Element 1: Identify potential areas of conflict			●			
Element 2: Maintain relationships with colleagues			●			

Plastering

Key
■ = Entry 3   ▲ = Level 1   ● = Level 2

Element	Reading	Writing	Speaking & Listening	Understanding and using mathematical information	Calculating and manipulating mathematical information	Interpreting results and communicating mathematical information
Unit MR 214: Prepare and mix materials						
Element 1: Select resources	▲		▲			
Element 2: Prepare and mix materials	▲ ●		▲			
Element 3: Comply with safe working practices	▲ ●		▲			
Unit MR 215: Prepare background surfaces						
Element 1: Select resources	▲		▲			
Element 2: Prepare background surfaces	▲ ●		▲			
Element 3: Comply with safe working practices	▲ ●		▲		▲	
Unit MR 216: Cut components to a dimension						
Element 1: Select resources for cutting	▲ ●		▲	▲	▲	
Element 2: Cut components to size	▲ ●		▲		▲	
Element 3: Comply with safe working practices	▲ ●		▲			

Plastering

Element	Reading	Writing	Speaking & Listening	Understanding and using mathematical information	Calculating and manipulating mathematical information	Interpreting results and communicating mathematical information
Unit MR 217: Contribute to producing plastering components						
Element 1: Select materials and components	▲		▲		▲	
Element 2: Contribute to producing plastering components	▲ ●		▲		▲	
Element 3: Comply with safe working practices	▲ ●		▲			
Unit MR 218: Apply materials to backgrounds						
Element 1: Select resources for use	▲ ●		▲			
Element 2: Prepare for and apply materials to surfaces	▲		▲		▲	
Element 3: Comply with safe working practices	▲ ●		▲			

6. Basic Skills Maps – Trowel Occupations

detailed maps of the Performance Criteria in each Element

Unit MR 01: Load and Unload resources

Element 1: Select resources

National Standard of Work	Literacy National Standard	Level Title	Numeracy National Standard	Level Title
1.1. you confirm that you understand your instructions	Read and understand straightforward texts of varying length on a variety of topics accurately and independently. Listen and respond to spoken language, including information and narratives, and follow explanations and instructions of varying length, adapting response to speaker, medium and context.	Reading Level 1 Speaking and Listening Level 1		
1.2. you ensure the selected quantity and quality of the resources are in accordance with the given instructions and, where they are unsuitable, take the necessary corrective action by reporting to the person in charge	Read and obtain information from different sources. Speak to communicate information, ideas and opinions adapting speech and content to take account of the listener(s) medium. Listen and respond to spoken language, including information and narratives, and follow explanations and instructions of varying length, adapting response to speaker, medium and context.	Reading Level 1 Speaking and Listening Level 1	Generate results to a given level of accuracy using methods, measures and checking procedures appropriate to the specified purpose – use whole numbers – use common measures.	Calculating and manipulating mathematical information Level 1

Unit MR 01: Load and unload resources

Element 2: Move resources manually

National Standard of Work	Literacy National Standard	Level Title	Numeracy National Standard	Level Title
2.1. you carry out your work practices to comply with the given instructions and you achieve the required movement of resources	Read and obtain information from different sources. Listen and respond to spoken language, including information and narratives, and follow explanations and instructions of varying length, adapting response to speaker, medium and context.	Reading Level 1 Speaking and Listening Level 1		
2.2. you put right any deficiencies in the stacking and positioning of resources by corrective action in accordance with the given instructions	Read and obtain information from different sources. Listen and respond to spoken language, including information and narratives, and follow explanations and instructions of varying length, adapting response to speaker, medium and context.	Reading Level 1 Speaking and Listening Level 1		
2.3. you carry out your work practices to comply with the given instructions to minimise the risk of damage to the resources and surrounding work area	Read and obtain information from different sources. Listen and respond to spoken language, including information and narratives, and follow explanations and instructions of varying length, adapting response to speaker, medium and context.	Reading Level 1 Speaking and Listening Level 1		
2.4. you comply with the given instructions when carrying out your work practices to maintain safe working procedures	Read and obtain information of varying length and detail from different sources. Listen and respond to spoken language, including information and narratives, and follow explanations and instructions of varying length, adapting response to speaker, medium and context.	Reading Level 2 Speaking and Listening Level 1		

Unit MR 01: Load and unload resources

Element 3: Comply with safe working practices

National Standard of Work	Literacy National Standard	Level Title	Numeracy National Standard	Level Title
3.1. you carry out your work practices to keep areas clean, free from debris and waste in accordance with the given instructions	Read and obtain information from different sources. Listen and respond to spoken language, including information and narratives, and follow explanations and instructions of varying length, adapting response to speaker, medium and context.	Reading Level 1 Speaking and Listening Level 1		
3.2. you identify any potential hazards relating to your work practices and take the necessary corrective action	Speak to communicate information, ideas and opinions adapting speech and content to take account of the listener(s) medium.	Speaking and Listening Level 1		
3.3. you carry out your work practices to comply with the given instructions to maintain safe and healthy working conditions	Read and obtain information of varying length and detail from different sources. Listen and respond to spoken language, including information and narratives, and follow explanations and instructions of varying length, adapting response to speaker, medium and context.	Reading Level 2 Speaking and Listening Level 1		

Getting the basics right in Construction (Common Occupations)

Unit MR 02: Contribute to erecting and dismantling working platforms

Element 1: Select resources

National Standard of Work	Literacy National Standard	Level Title	Numeracy National Standard	Level Title
1.1. you confirm that you understand your instructions	Read and understand straightforward texts of varying length on a variety of topics accurately and independently. Listen and respond to spoken language, including information and narratives, and follow explanations and instructions of varying length, adapting response to speaker, medium and context.	Reading Level 1 Speaking and Listening Level 1		
1.2. you ensure the selected quantify and quality of the resources are in accordance with the given instructions and, where they are unsuitable, take the necessary corrective action by reporting to the person in charge	Read and obtain information from different sources. Speak to communicate information, ideas and opinions adapting speech and content to take account of the listener(s) medium. Listen and respond to spoken language, including information and narratives, and follow explanations and instructions of varying length, adapting response to speaker, medium and context.	Reading Level 1 Speaking and Listening Level 1	Generate results to a given level of accuracy usIng methods, measures and checking procedures appropriate to the specified purpose – use whole numbers – use common measures.	Calculating and manipulating mathematical information Level 1

Unit MR 02: Contribute to erecting and dismantling working platforms

Element 2: Assist with erecting and dismantling access equipment

National Standard of Work	Literacy National Standard	Level Title	Numeracy National Standard	Level Title
2.1. you carry out your work practices to comply with the given instructions and you achieve a safe working platform	Read and obtain information from different sources. Listen and respond to spoken language, including information and narratives, and follow explanations and instructions of varying length, adapting response to speaker, medium and context.	Reading Level 1 Speaking and Listening Level 1		
2.2. you put right any deficiencies in the quality of your work by corrective action in accordance with the given instructions	Read and obtain information from different sources. Listen and respond to spoken language, including information and narratives, and follow explanations and instructions of varying length, adapting response to speaker, medium and context.	Reading Level 1 Speaking and Listening Level 1		
2.3. you carry out your work practices to comply with the given instructions to minimise the risk of damage to the work and surrounding work area	Read and obtain information from different sources. Listen and respond to spoken language, including information and narratives, and follow explanations and instructions of varying length, adapting response to speaker, medium and context.	Reading Level 1 Speaking and Listening Level 1		
2.4. you comply with the given instructions when carrying out your work practices to maintain safe working procedures	Read and obtain information of varying length and detail from different sources. Listen and respond to spoken language, including information and narratives, and follow explanations and instructions of varying length, adapting response to speaker, medium and context.	Reading Level 2 Speaking and Listening Level 1		

Getting the basics right in Construction (Common Occupations)

Unit MR 02: Contribute to erecting and dismantling working platforms

Element 3: Comply with safe working practices

National Standard of Work	Literacy National Standard	Level Title	Numeracy National Standard	Level Title
3.1. you carry out your work practices to keep areas clean, free from debris and waste in accordance with the given instructions	Read and obtain information from different sources. Listen and respond to spoken language, including information and narratives, and follow explanations and instructions of varying length, adapting response to speaker, medium and context.	Reading Level 1 Speaking and Listening Level 1		
3.2. you identify any potential hazards relating to your work practices and take the necessary corrective action	Speak to communicate information, ideas and opinions adapting speech and content to take account of the listener(s) medium.	Speaking and Listening Level 1		
3.3. you carry out your work practices to comply with the given instructions to maintain safe and healthy working conditions	Read and obtain information of varying length and detail from different sources. Listen and respond to spoken language, including information and narratives, and follow explanations and instructions of varying length, adapting response to speaker, medium and context.	Reading Level 2 Speaking and Listening Level 1		

Unit MR 03: Contribute to maintaining work relationships

Element 1: Identify potential areas of conflict

National Standard of Work	Literacy National Standard	Level Title	Numeracy National Standard	Level Title
1.1. conflicts resulting from work practices relating to your colleagues are resolved by corrective action	Engage in discussion with one or more people in a variety of different situations, making clear and effective contributions that produce outcomes appropriate to purpose and topic.	Speaking and Listening Level 1		
1.2. areas of potential conflicts are identified and dealt with by corrective action before problems arise	Engage in discussion with one or more people in a variety of different situations, making clear and effective contributions that produce outcomes appropriate to purpose and topic.	Speaking and Listening Level 2		
1.3. you carry out your work practices to avoid causing conflicts with your colleagues	Engage in discussion with one or more people in a variety of different situations, making clear and effective contributions that produce outcomes appropriate to purpose and topic.	Speaking and Listening Level 2		

Getting the basics right in Construction (Common Occupations)

Unit MR 03: Contribute to maintaining work relationships

Element 2: Maintain relationships with colleagues

National Standard of Work	Literacy National Standard	Level Title	Numeracy National Standard	Level Title
2.1. your relationships with colleagues are maintained during work practices to achieve the required productivity	Engage in discussion with one or more people in familiar and unfamiliar situations, making clear and relevant contributions that respond to what others say and produce a shared understanding about different topics.	Speaking and Listening Level 2		
2.2. time is taken to establish and maintain constructive relationships with your colleagues	Speak to communicate information, ideas and opinions adapting speech and content to take account of the listener(s) medium.	Speaking and Listening Level 2		
2.3. you carry out your work practices to take account of views and opinions of your colleagues	Listen and respond to spoken language, including extended information and narratives, and follow detailed explanations and multi-step instructions of varying length, adapting response to speaker, medium and context.	Speaking and Listening Level 2		

Unit MR 180: Prepare and mix materials

Element 1: Select materials

National Standard of Work	Literacy National Standard	Level Title	Numeracy National Standard	Level Title
1.1. you confirm that you understand your instructions	Read and understand straightforward texts of varying length on a variety of topics accurately and independently. Listen and respond to spoken language, including information and narratives, and follow explanations and instructions of varying length, adapting response to speaker, medium and context.	Reading Level 1 Speaking and Listening Level 1		
1.2. you ensure the selected quantity and quality of the resources are in accordance with the given instructions and where they are unsuitable, take the necessary corrective action by reporting to the person in charge	Read and obtain information from different sources. Speak to communicate information, ideas and opinions adapting speech and content to take account of the listener(s) medium. Listen and respond to spoken language, including information and narratives, and follow explanations and instructions of varying length, adapting response to speaker, medium and context.	Reading Level 1 Speaking and Listening Level 1 Speaking and Listening Level 1	Generate results to a given level of accuracy using methods, measures and checking procedures appropriate to the specified purpose – use whole numbers – use common measures.	Calculating and manipulating mathematical information Level 1

Unit MR 180: Prepare and mix materials

Element 2: Mix materials

National Standard of Work	Literacy National Standard	Level Title	Numeracy National Standard	Level Title
2.1. you carry out your work practices to comply with the given instructions and you achieve the required quality of finish to your work	Read and obtain information from different sources. Listen and respond to spoken language, including information and narratives, and follow explanations and instructions of varying length, adapting response to speaker, medium and context.	Reading Level 1 Speaking and Listening Level 1	Generate results to a given level of accuracy using methods, measures and checking procedures appropriate to the specified purpose – use whole numbers – use common measures.	Calculating and manipulating mathematical information Level 1
2.2. you put right any deficiencies in the quality of your work by corrective action in accordance with the given instructions	Read and obtain information from different sources. Listen and respond to spoken language, including information and narratives, and follow explanations and instructions of varying length, adapting response to speaker, medium and context.	Reading Level 1 Speaking and Listening Level 1		
2.3. you carry out your work practices to comply with the given instructions to minimise the risk of damage to the work and surrounding work area	Read and obtain information from different sources. Listen and respond to spoken language, including information and narratives, and follow explanations and instructions of varying length, adapting response to speaker, medium and context.	Reading Level 1 Speaking and Listening Level 1		
2.4. you comply with the given instructions when carrying out your work practices to maintain safe working procedures	Read and obtain information of varying length and detail from different sources. Listen and respond to spoken language, including information and narratives, and follow explanations and instructions of varying length, adapting response to speaker, medium and context.	Reading Level 2 Speaking and Listening Level 1		

Unit MR 180: Prepare and mix materials

Element 3: Comply with safe working practices

National Standard of Work	Literacy National Standard	Level Title	Numeracy National Standard	Level Title
3.1. you carry out your work practices to keep areas clean, free from debris and waste in accordance with the given instructions	Read and obtain information from different sources. Listen and respond to spoken language, including information and narratives, and follow explanations and instructions of varying length, adapting response to speaker, medium and context.	Reading Level 1 Speaking and Listening Level 1		
3.2. you identify any potential hazards relating to your work practices and take the necessary corrective action	Speak to communicate information, ideas and opinions adapting speech and content to take account of the listener(s) medium.	Speaking and Listening Level 1		
3.3. you carry out your work practices to comply with the given instructions to maintain safe and healthy working conditions	Read and obtain information of varying length and detail from different sources. Listen and respond to spoken language, including information and narratives, and follow explanations and instructions of varying length, adapting response to speaker, medium and context.	Reading Level 2 Speaking and Listening Level 1		

Unit MR 181: Prepare components

Element 1: Select components

National Standard of Work	Literacy National Standard	Level Title	Numeracy National Standard	Level Title
1.1. you confirm that you understand your instructions	Read and understand straightforward texts of varying length on a variety of topics accurately and independently. Listen and respond to spoken language, including information and narratives, and follow explanations and instructions of varying length, adapting response to speaker, medium and context.	Reading Level 1 Speaking and Listening Level 1		
1.2. you ensure the selected quantity and quality of the resources are in accordance with the given instructions and where they are unsuitable, take the necessary corrective action by reporting to the person in charge	Read and obtain information from different sources. Speak to communicate information, ideas and opinions adapting speech and content to take account of the listener(s) medium. Listen and respond to spoken language, including information and narratives, and follow explanations and instructions of varying length, adapting response to speaker, medium and context.	Reading Level 1 Speaking and Listening Level 1 Speaking and Listening Level 1	Generate results to a given level of accuracy using methods, measures and checking procedures appropriate to the specified purpose – use whole numbers – use common measures.	Calculating and manipulating mathematical information Level 1

Unit MR 181: Prepare components

Element 2: Mark out and cut components

National Standard of Work	Literacy National Standard	Level Title	Numeracy National Standard	Level Title
2.1. you carry out your work practices to comply with the given instructions and you achieve the required quality of finish to your work	Read and obtain information from different sources. Listen and respond to spoken language, including information and narratives, and follow explanations and instructions of varying length, adapting response to speaker, medium and context.	Reading Level 1 Speaking and Listening Level 1		
2.2. you put right any deficiencies in the quality of your work by corrective action in accordance with the given instructions	Read and obtain information from different sources. Listen and respond to spoken language, including information and narratives, and follow explanations and instructions of varying length, adapting response to speaker, medium and context.	Reading Level 1 Speaking and Listening Level 1		
2.3. you carry out your work practices to comply with the given instructions to minimise the risk of damage to the work and surrounding work area	Read and obtain information from different sources. Listen and respond to spoken language, including information and narratives, and follow explanations and instructions of varying length, adapting response to speaker, medium and context.	Reading Level 1 Speaking and Listening Level 1		
2.4. you comply with the given instructions when carrying out your work practices to maintain safe working procedures	Read and obtain information of varying length and detail from different sources. Listen and respond to spoken language, including information and narratives, and follow explanations and instructions of varying length, adapting response to speaker, medium and context.	Reading Level 2 Speaking and Listening Level 1		

Getting the basics right in Construction (Common Occupations)

Unit MR 181: Prepare components

Element 3: Comply with safe working practices

National Standard of Work	Literacy National Standard	Level Title	Numeracy National Standard	Level Title
3.1. you carry out your work practices to keep areas clean, free from debris and waste in accordance with the given instructions	Read and obtain information from different sources. Listen and respond to spoken language, including information and narratives, and follow explanations and instructions of varying length, adapting response to speaker, medium and context.	Reading Level 1 Speaking and Listening Level 1		
3.2. you identify any potential hazards relating to your work practices and take the necessary corrective action	Speak to communicate information, ideas and opinions adapting speech and content to take account of the listener(s) medium.	Speaking and Listening Level 1		
3.3. you carry out your work practices to comply with the given instructions to maintain safe and healthy working conditions	Read and obtain information of varying length and detail from different sources. Listen and respond to spoken language, including information and narratives, and follow explanations and instructions of varying length, adapting response to speaker, medium and context.	Reading Level 2 Speaking and Listening Level 1		

Unit MR 182: Position components to line

Element 1: Select materials and components

National Standard of Work	Literacy National Standard	Level Title	Numeracy National Standard	Level Title
1.1. you confirm that you understand your instructions	Read and understand straightforward texts of varying length on a variety of topics accurately and independently.	Reading Level 1		
	Listen and respond to spoken language, including information and narratives, and follow explanations and instructions of varying length, adapting response to speaker, medium and context.	Speaking and Listening Level 1		
1.2. you ensure the selected quantity and quality of the resources are in accordance with the given instructions and where they are unsuitable, take the necessary corrective action by reporting to the person in charge	Read and obtain information from different sources.	Reading Level 1	Generate results to a given level of accuracy using methods, measures and checking procedures appropriate to the specified purpose – use whole numbers – use common measures.	Calculating and manipulating mathematical information Level 1
	Speak to communicate information, ideas and opinions adapting speech and content to take account of the listener(s) medium.	Speaking and Listening Level 1		
	Listen and respond to spoken language, including information and narratives, and follow explanations and instructions of varying length, adapting response to speaker, medium and context.	Speaking and Listening Level 1		

Unit MR 182: Position components to line

Element 2: Position components

National Standard of Work	Literacy National Standard	Level Title	Numeracy National Standard	Level Title
2.1. you carry out your work practices to comply with the given instructions and you achieve the required quality of finish to your work	Read and obtain information from different sources. Listen and respond to spoken language, including information and narratives, and follow explanations and instructions of varying length, adapting response to speaker, medium and context.	Reading Level 1 Speaking and Listening Level 1	Generate results to a given level of accuracy using methods, measures and checking procedures appropriate to the specified purpose – use whole numbers – use common measures.	Calculating and manipulating mathematical information Level 1
2.2. you put right any deficiencies in the quality of your work by corrective action In accordance with the given instructions	Read and obtain information from different sources. Listen and respond to spoken language, including information and narratives, and follow explanations and instructions of varying length, adapting response to speaker, medium and context.	Reading Level 1 Speaking and Listening Level 1		
2.3. you carry out your work practices to comply with the given instructions to minimise the risk of damage to the work and surrounding work area	Read and obtain information from different sources. Listen and respond to spoken language, including information and narratives, and follow explanations and instructions of varying length, adapting response to speaker, medium and context.	Reading Level 1 Speaking and Listening Level 1		
2.4. you comply with the given instructions when carrying out your work practices to maintain safe working procedures	Read and obtain information of varying length and detail from different sources. Listen and respond to spoken language, including information and narratives, and follow explanations and instructions of varying length, adapting response to speaker, medium and context.	Reading Level 2 Speaking and Listening Level 1		

Unit MR 182: Position components to line

Element 3: Comply with safe working practices

National Standard of Work	Literacy National Standard	Level Title	Numeracy National Standard	Level Title
3.1. you carry out your work practices to keep areas clean, free from debris and waste in accordance with the given instructions	Read and obtain information from different sources. Listen and respond to spoken language, including information and narratives, and follow explanations and instructions of varying length, adapting response to speaker, medium and context.	Reading Level 1 Speaking and Listening Level 1		
3.2. you identify any potential hazards relating to your work practices and take the necessary corrective action	Speak to communicate information, ideas and opinions adapting speech and content to take account of the listener(s) medium.	Speaking and Listening Level 1		
3.3. you carry out your work practices to comply with the given instructions to maintain safe and healthy working conditions	Read and obtain information of varying length and detail from different sources. Listen and respond to spoken language, including information and narratives, and follow explanations and instructions of varying length, adapting response to speaker, medium and context.	Reading Level 2 Speaking and Listening Level 1		

Unit MR 183: Contribute to setting out positions

Element 1: Select resources

National Standard of Work	Literacy National Standard	Level Title	Numeracy National Standard	Level Title
1.1. you confirm that you understand your instructions	Read and understand straightforward texts of varying length on a variety of topics accurately and independently. Listen and respond to spoken language, including information and narratives, and follow explanations and instructions of varying length, adapting response to speaker, medium and context.	Reading Level 1 Speaking and Listening Level 1		
1.2. you ensure the selected quantity and quality of the resources are in accordance with the given instructions and where they are unsuitable, take the necessary corrective action by reporting to the person in charge	Read and obtain information from different sources. Speak to communicate information, ideas and opinions adapting speech and content to take account of the listener(s) medium. Listen and respond to spoken language, including information and narratives, and follow explanations and instructions of varying length, adapting response to speaker, medium and context.	Reading Level 1 Speaking and Listening Level 1 Speaking and Listening Level 1	Generate results to a given level of accuracy using methods, measures and checking procedures appropriate to the specified purpose – use whole numbers – use common measures.	Calculating and manipulating mathematical information Level 1

Unit MR 183: Contribute to setting out positions

Element 2: Contribute to setting out work

National Standard of Work	Literacy National Standard	Level Title	Numeracy National Standard	Level Title
2.1. you carry out your work practices to comply with the given instructions and you achieve the required quality of finish to your work	Read and obtain information from different sources. Listen and respond to spoken language, including information and narratives, and follow explanations and instructions of varying length, adapting response to speaker, medium and context.	Reading Level 1 Speaking and Listening Level 1	Generate results to a given level of accuracy using methods, measures and checking procedures appropriate to the specified purpose – use whole numbers – use common measures.	Calculating and manipulating mathematical information Level 1
2.2. you put right any deficiencies in the quality of your work by corrective action in accordance with the given instructions	Read and obtain information from different sources. Listen and respond to spoken language, including information and narratives, and follow explanations and instructions of varying length, adapting response to speaker, medium and context.	Reading Level 1 Speaking and Listening Level 1		
2.3. you carry out your work practices to comply with the given instructions to minimise the risk of damage to the work and surrounding work area	Read and obtain information from different sources. Listen and respond to spoken language, including information and narratives, and follow explanations and instructions of varying length, adapting response to speaker, medium and context.	Reading Level 1 Speaking and Listening Level 1		
2.4. you comply with the given instructions when carrying out your work practices to maintain safe working procedures	Read and obtain information of varying length and detail from different sources. Listen and respond to spoken language, including information and narratives, and follow explanations and instructions of varying length, adapting response to speaker, medium and context.	Reading Level 2 Speaking and Listening Level 1		

Unit MR 183: Contribute to setting out positions

Element 3: Comply with safe working practices

National Standard of Work	Literacy National Standard	Level Title	Numeracy National Standard	Level Title
3.1. you carry out your work practices to keep areas clean, free from debris and waste in accordance with the given instructions	Read and obtain information from different sources. Listen and respond to spoken language, including information and narratives, and follow explanations and instructions of varying length, adapting response to speaker, medium and context.	Reading Level 1 Speaking and Listening Level 1		
3.2. you identify any potential hazards relating to your work practices and take the necessary corrective action	Speak to communicate information, ideas and opinions adapting speech and content to take account of the listener(s) medium.	Speaking and Listening Level 1		
3.3. you carry out your work practices to comply with the given instructions to maintain safe and healthy working conditions	Read and obtain information of varying length and detail from different sources. Listen and respond to spoken language, including information and narratives, and follow explanations and instructions of varying length, adapting response to speaker, medium and context.	Reading Level 2 Speaking and Listening Level 1		

Unit MR 184: Contribute to laying concrete

Element 1: Select resources

National Standard of Work	Literacy National Standard	Level Title	Numeracy National Standard	Level Title
1.1. you confirm that you understand your instructions	Read and understand straightforward texts of varying length on a variety of topics accurately and independently. Listen and respond to spoken language, including information and narratives, and follow explanations and instructions of varying length, adapting response to speaker, medium and context.	Reading Level 1 Speaking and Listening Level 1		
1.2. you ensure the selected quantity and quality of the resources are in accordance with the given instructions and where they are unsuitable, take the necessary corrective action by reporting to the person in charge	Read and obtain information from different sources. Speak to communicate information, ideas and opinions adapting speech and content to take account of the listener(s) medium. Listen and respond to spoken language, including information and narratives, and follow explanations and instructions of varying length, adapting response to speaker, medium and context.	Reading Level 1 Speaking and Listening Level 1 Speaking and Listening Level 1	Generate results to a given level of accuracy using methods, measures and checking procedures appropriate to the specified purpose – use whole numbers – use common measures.	Calculating and manipulating mathematical information Level 1

Unit MR 184: Contribute to laying concrete

Element 2: Contribute to concreting work

National Standard of Work	Literacy National Standard	Level Title	Numeracy National Standard	Level Title
2.1. you carry out your work practices to comply with the given instructions and you achieve the required quality of finish to your work	Read and obtain information from different sources. Listen and respond to spoken language, including information and narratives, and follow explanations and instructions of varying length, adapting response to speaker, medium and context.	Reading Level 1 Speaking and Listening Level 1		
2.2. you put right any deficiencies in the quality of your work by corrective action in accordance with the given instructions	Read and obtain information from different sources. Listen and respond to spoken language, including information and narratives, and follow explanations and instructions of varying length, adapting response to speaker, medium and context.	Reading Level 1 Speaking and Listening Level 1		
2.3. you carry out your work practices to comply with the given instructions to minimise the risk of damage to the work and surrounding work area	Read and obtain information from different sources. Listen and respond to spoken language, including information and narratives, and follow explanations and instructions of varying length, adapting response to speaker, medium and context.	Reading Level 1 Speaking and Listening Level 1		
2.4. you comply with the given instructions when carrying out your work practices to maintain safe working procedures	Read and obtain information of varying length and detail from different sources. Listen and respond to spoken language, including information and narratives, and follow explanations and instructions of varying length, adapting response to speaker, medium and context.	Reading Level 2 Speaking and Listening Level 1		

Unit MR 184: Contribute to laying concrete

Element 3: Comply with safe working practices

National Standard of Work	Literacy National Standard	Level Title	Numeracy National Standard	Level Title
3.1. you carry out your work practices to keep areas clean, free from debris and waste in accordance with the given instructions	Read and obtain information from different sources. Listen and respond to spoken language, including information and narratives, and follow explanations and instructions of varying length, adapting response to speaker, medium and context.	Reading Level 1 Speaking and Listening Level 1		
3.2. you identify any potential hazards relating to your work practices and take the necessary corrective action	Speak to communicate information, ideas and opinions adapting speech and content to take account of the listener(s) medium.	Speaking and Listening Level 1		
3.3. you carry out your work practices to comply with the given instructions to maintain safe and healthy working conditions	Read and obtain information of varying length and detail from different sources. Listen and respond to spoken language, including information and narratives, and follow explanations and instructions of varying length, adapting response to speaker, medium and context.	Reading Level 2 Speaking and Listening Level 1		

Unit MR 185: Contribute to forming surface finishes

Element 1: Select resources

National Standard of Work	Literacy National Standard	Level Title	Numeracy National Standard	Level Title
1.1. you confirm that you understand your instructions	Read and understand straightforward texts of varying length on a variety of topics accurately and independently. Listen and respond to spoken language, including information and narratives, and follow explanations and instructions of varying length, adapting response to speaker, medium and context.	Reading Level 1 Speaking and Listening Level 1		
1.2. you ensure the selected quantity and quality of the resources are in accordance with the given instructions and where they are unsuitable, take the necessary corrective action by reporting to the person in charge	Read and obtain information from different sources. Speak to communicate information, ideas and opinions adapting speech and content to take account of the listener(s) medium. Listen and respond to spoken language, including information and narratives, and follow explanations and instructions of varying length, adapting response to speaker, medium and context.	Reading Level 1 Speaking and Listening Level 1 Speaking and Listening Level 1	Generate results to a given level of accuracy using methods, measures and checking procedures appropriate to the specified purpose – use whole numbers – use common measures.	Calculating and manipulating mathematical information Level 1

Unit PR 07: Carry out slinging and signalling for the movement of loads

Element 1: Prepare and sling loads for lifting

National Standard of Work	Literacy National Standard	Level Title	Numeracy National Standard	Level Title
1.1. loads being moved are accurately identified from relevant information and instruction	Listen and respond to spoken language, including information and narratives, and follow explanations and instructions of varying length, adapting response to speaker, medium and context. Read and obtain information from different sources.	Speaking and Listening Level 1 Reading Level 1		
1.2. slinging technique is chosen in accordance with the characteristics of the loads, the intended lift and approved procedures and practices	Read and obtain information from different sources.	Reading Level 1		
1.3. difficulties in carrying out the slinging and movement of loads are identified and clarified with the appropriate person(s)	Speak to communicate information, ideas and opinions adapting speech and content to take account of the listener(s) medium.	Speaking and Listening Level 1		
1.4. slinging equipment is selected and confirmed suitable for load(s) to be lifted				
1.5. defects and faults relating to the slinging equipment are reported to the authorised person				
1.6. loads are prepared and slung in accordance with the chosen slinging technique	Read and obtain information from different sources.	Reading Level 1		
1.7. support and balance of the slung load is confirmed satisfactory and secure prior to movement	Speak to communicate information, ideas and opinions adapting speech and content to take account of the listener(s) medium.	Speaking and Listening Level 1		
1.8. work is carried out to approved procedures and practices and in compliance with statutory requirements	Read and obtain information of varying length and detail from different sources.	Speaking and Listening Level 2		

Getting the basics right in Construction (Common Occupations)

Unit PR 07: Carry out slinging and signalling for the movement of loads

Element 2: Direct and control the movement and placing of loads

National Standard of Work	Literacy National Standard	Level Title	Numeracy National Standard	Level Title
2.1. load movement and operations procedure are agreed with relevant personnel	Read and obtain information from different sources. Speak to communicate information, ideas and opinions adapting speech and content to take account of the listener(s) medium.	Reading Level 1 Speaking and Listening Level 1		
2.2. method of signalling and communication is confirmed and established with relevant personnel prior to the commencement of any movement operations	Speak to communicate information, ideas and opinions adapting speech and content to take account of the listener(s) medium.	Speaking and Listening Level 1		
2.3. signalling and communication are carried out in accordance with approved procedures and practices	Read and obtain information from different sources.	Reading Level 1		
2.4. movement of load is directed to its destination accurately using agreed signalling code	N/A			
2.5. unclear signalling and communication are responded to promptly and clarified so as not to endanger personnel or operations	Speak to communicate information, ideas and opinions adapting speech and content to take account of the listener(s) medium.	Speaking and Listening Level 1		
2.6. stability of load is monitored throughout movement and on release of load	N/A			
2.7. load is positioned, set down and the sling relaxed for the removal of the lifting equipment	N/A			
2.8. work is carried out to approved procedures and practices and in compliance with statutory requirements	Read and obtain information of varying length and detail from different sources.	Reading Level 2		

Basic Skills Maps — Wood Occupations

detailed maps of the Performance Criteria in each Element

Unit MR 01: Load and Unload resources

Element 1: Select resources

National Standard of Work	Literacy National Standard	Level Title	Numeracy National Standard	Level Title
1.1. you confirm that you understand your instructions	Read and understand straightforward texts of varying length on a variety of topics accurately and independently. Listen and respond to spoken language, including information and narratives, and follow explanations and instructions of varying length, adapting response to speaker, medium and context.	Reading Level 1 Speaking and Listening Level 1		
1.2. you ensure the selected quantity and quality of the resources are in accordance with the given instructions and, where they are unsuitable, take the necessary corrective action by reporting to the person in charge	Read and obtain information from different sources. Speak to communicate information, ideas and opinions adapting speech and content to take account of the listener(s) medium. Listen and respond to spoken language, including information and narratives, and follow explanations and instructions of varying length, adapting response to speaker, medium and context.	Reading Level 1 Speaking and Listening Level 1	Generate results to a given level of accuracy using methods, measures and checking procedures appropriate to the specified purpose − use whole numbers − use common measures.	Calculating and manipulating mathematical information Level 1

Unit MR 01: Load and unload resources

Element 2: Move resources manually

National Standard of Work	Literacy National Standard	Level Title	Numeracy National Standard	Level Title
2.1. you carry out your work practices to comply with the given instructions and you achieve the required movement of resources	Read and obtain information from different sources. Listen and respond to spoken language, including information and narratives, and follow explanations and instructions of varying length, adapting response to speaker, medium and context.	Reading Level 1 Speaking and Listening Level 1		
2.2. you put right any deficiencies in the stacking and positioning of resources by corrective action in accordance with the given instructions	Read and obtain information from different sources. Listen and respond to spoken language, including information and narratives, and follow explanations and instructions of varying length, adapting response to speaker, medium and context.	Reading Level 1 Speaking and Listening Level 1		
2.3. you carry out your work practices to comply with the given instructions to minimise the risk of damage to the resources and surrounding work area	Read and obtain information from different sources. Listen and respond to spoken language, including information and narratives, and follow explanations and instructions of varying length, adapting response to speaker, medium and context.	Reading Level 1 Speaking and Listening Level 1		
2.4. you comply with the given instructions when carrying out your work practices to maintain safe working procedures	Read and obtain information of varying length and detail from different sources. Listen and respond to spoken language, including information and narratives, and follow explanations and instructions of varying length, adapting response to speaker, medium and context.	Reading Level 2 Speaking and Listening Level 1		

Unit MR 01: Load and unload resources

Element 3: Comply with safe working practices

National Standard of Work	Literacy National Standard	Level Title	Numeracy National Standard	Level Title
3.1. you carry out your work practices to keep areas clean, free from debris and waste in accordance with the given instructions	Read and obtain information from different sources. Listen and respond to spoken language, including information and narratives, and follow explanations and instructions of varying length, adapting response to speaker, medium and context.	Reading Level 1 Speaking and Listening Level 1		
3.2. you identify any potential hazards relating to your work practices and take the necessary corrective action	Speak to communicate information, ideas and opinions adapting speech and content to take account of the listener(s) medium.	Speaking and Listening Level 1		
3.3. you carry out your work practices to comply with the given instructions to maintain safe and healthy working conditions	Read and obtain information of varying length and detail from different sources. Listen and respond to spoken language, including information and narratives, and follow explanations and instructions of varying length, adapting response to speaker, medium and context.	Reading Level 2 Speaking and Listening Level 1		

Getting the basics right in Construction (Common Occupations)

Unit MR 02: Contribute to erecting and dismantling working platforms

Element 1: Select resources

National Standard of Work	Literacy National Standard	Level Title	Numeracy National Standard	Level Title
1.1. you confirm that you understand your instructions	Read and understand straightforward texts of varying length on a variety of topics accurately and independently. Listen and respond to spoken language, including information and narratives, and follow explanations and instructions of varying length, adapting response to speaker, medium and context.	Reading Level 1 Speaking and Listening Level 1		
1.2. you ensure the selected quantify and quality of the resources are in accordance with the given instructions and, where they are unsuitable, take the necessary corrective action by reporting to the person in charge	Read and obtain information from different sources. Speak to communicate information, ideas and opinions adapting speech and content to take account of the listener(s) medium. Listen and respond to spoken language, including information and narratives, and follow explanations and instructions of varying length, adapting response to speaker, medium and context.	Reading Level 1 Speaking and Listening Level 1	Generate results to a given level of accuracy using methods, measures and checking procedures appropriate to the specified purpose – use whole numbers – use common measures.	Calculating and manipulating mathematical information Level 1

Unit MR 02: Contribute to erecting and dismantling working platforms

Element 2: Assist with erecting and dismantling access equipment

National Standard of Work	Literacy National Standard	Level Title	Numeracy National Standard	Level Title
2.1. you carry out your work practices to comply with the given instructions and you achieve a safe working platform	Read and obtain information from different sources. Listen and respond to spoken language, including information and narratives, and follow explanations and instructions of varying length, adapting response to speaker, medium and context.	Reading Level 1 Speaking and Listening Level 1		
2.2. you put right any deficiencies in the quality of your work by corrective action in accordance with the given instructions	Read and obtain information from different sources. Listen and respond to spoken language, including information and narratives, and follow explanations and instructions of varying length, adapting response to speaker, medium and context.	Reading Level 1 Speaking and Listening Level 1		
2.3. you carry out your work practices to comply with the given instructions to minimise the risk of damage to the work and surrounding work area	Read and obtain information from different sources. Listen and respond to spoken language, including information and narratives, and follow explanations and instructions of varying length, adapting response to speaker, medium and context.	Reading Level 1 Speaking and Listening Level 1		
2.4. you comply with the given instructions when carrying out your work practices to maintain safe working procedures	Read and obtain information of varying length and detail from different sources. Listen and respond to spoken language, including information and narratives, and follow explanations and instructions of varying length, adapting response to speaker, medium and context.	Reading Level 2 Speaking and Listening Level 1		

Getting the basics right in Construction (Common Occupations)

Unit MR 02: Contribute to erecting and dismantling working platforms

Element 3: Comply with safe working practices

National Standard of Work	Literacy National Standard	Level Title	Numeracy National Standard	Level Title
3.1. you carry out your work practices to keep areas clean, free from debris and waste in accordance with the given instructions	Read and obtain information from different sources. Listen and respond to spoken language, including information and narratives, and follow explanations and instructions of varying length, adapting response to speaker, medium and context.	Reading Level 1 Speaking and Listening Level 1		
3.2. you identify any potential hazards relating to your work practices and take the necessary corrective action	Speak to communicate information, ideas and opinions adapting speech and content to take account of the listener(s) medium.	Speaking and Listening Level 1		
3.3. you carry out your work practices to comply with the given instructions to maintain safe and healthy working conditions	Read and obtain information of varying length and detail from different sources. Listen and respond to spoken language, including information and narratives, and follow explanations and instructions of varying length, adapting response to speaker, medium and context.	Reading Level 2 Speaking and Listening Level 1		

Unit MR 03: Contribute to maintaining work relationships

Element 1: Identify potential areas of conflict

National Standard of Work	Literacy National Standard	Level Title	Numeracy National Standard	Level Title
1.1. conflicts resulting from work practices relating to your colleagues are resolved by corrective action	Engage in discussion with one or more people in a variety of different situations, making clear and effective contributions that produce outcomes appropriate to purpose and topic.	Speaking and Listening Level 2		
1.2. areas of potential conflicts are identified and dealt with by corrective action before problems arise	Engage in discussion with one or more people in a variety of different situations, making clear and effective contributions that produce outcomes appropriate to purpose and topic.	Speaking and Listening Level 2		
1.3. you carry out your work practices to avoid causing conflicts with your colleagues	Engage in discussion with one or more people in a variety of different situations, making clear and effective contributions that produce outcomes appropriate to purpose and topic.	Speaking and Listening Level 2		

Getting the basics right in Construction (Common Occupations)

Unit MR 03: Contribute to maintaining work relationships

Element 2: Maintain relationships with colleagues

National Standard of Work	Literacy National Standard	Level Title	Numeracy National Standard	Level Title
2.1. your relationships with colleagues are maintained during work practices to achieve the required productivity	Engage in discussion with one or more people in familiar and unfamiliar situations, making clear and relevant contributions that respond to what others say and produce a shared understanding about different topics.	Speaking and Listening Level 2		
2.2. time is taken to establish and maintain constructive relationships with your colleagues	Speak to communicate information, ideas and opinions adapting speech and content to take account of the listener(s) medium.	Speaking and Listening Level 2		
2.3. you carry out your work practices to take account of views and opinions of your colleagues	Listen and respond to spoken language, including extended information and narratives, and follow detailed explanations and multi-step instructions of varying length, adapting response to speaker, medium and context.	Speaking and Listening Level 2		

Unit MR 05: Set up and use portable power tools

Element 1: Select resources

National Standard of Work	Literacy National Standard	Level Title	Numeracy National Standard	Level Title
1.1. you confirm that you understand your instructions	Read and understand straightforward texts of varying length on a variety of topics accurately and independently. Listen and respond to spoken language, including information and narratives, and follow explanations and instructions of varying length, adapting response to speaker, medium and context.	Reading Level 1 Speaking and Listening Level 1		
1.2. you ensure the selected quantity and quality of the resources are in accordance with the given instructions and, where they are unsuitable, take the necessary corrective action by reporting to the person in charge	Read and obtain information from different sources. Speak to communicate information, ideas and opinions adapting speech and content to take account of the listener(s) medium. Listen and respond to spoken language, including information and narratives, and follow explanations and instructions of varying length, adapting response to speaker, medium and context.	Reading Level 1 Speaking and Listening Level 1	Generate results to a given level of accuracy using methods, measures and checking procedures appropriate to the specified purpose – use whole numbers – use common measures.	Calculating and manipulating mathematical information Level 1

Unit MR 05: Set up and use portable power tools

Element 2: Operate power tools

National Standard of Work	Literacy National Standard	Level Title	Numeracy National Standard	Level Title
2.1. you carry out your work practices to comply with the given instructions and you achieve the required quality of finish to your work	Read and obtain information from different sources. Listen and respond to spoken language, including information and narratives, and follow explanations and instructions of varying length, adapting response to speaker, medium and context.	Reading Level 1 Speaking and Listening Level 1	Generate results to a given level of accuracy using methods, measures and checking procedures appropriate to the specified purpose – use whole numbers – use common measures.	Calculating and manipulating mathematical information Level 1
2.2. you put right any deficiencies in the quality of your work by corrective action In accordance with the given instructions	Read and obtain information from different sources. LIsten and respond to spoken language, including information and narratives, and follow explanations and instructions of varying length, adapting response to speaker, medium and context.	Reading Level 1 SpeakIng and Listening Level 1		
2.3. you carry out your work practices to comply with the given instructions to minimise the risk of damage to the resources and surrounding work area	Read and obtain information from different sources. Listen and respond to spoken language, including information and narratives, and follow explanations and instructions of varying length, adapting response to speaker, medium and context.	Reading Level 1 Speaking and Listening Level 1		
2.4. you comply with the given instructions when carrying out your work practices to maintain safe working procedures	Read and obtain information of varying length and detail from different sources. Listen and respond to spoken language, including information and narratives, and follow explanations and instructions of varying length, adapting response to speaker, medium and context.	Reading Level 2 Speaking and Listening Level 1		

Unit MR 05: Set up and use portable power tools

Element 3: Comply with safe working practices

National Standard of Work	Literacy National Standard	Level Title	Numeracy National Standard	Level Title
3.1. you carry out your work practices to keep areas clean, free from debris and waste in accordance with the given instructions	Read and obtain information from different sources. Listen and respond to spoken language, including information and narratives, and follow explanations and instructions of varying length, adapting response to speaker, medium and context.	Reading Level 1 Speaking and Listening Level 1		
3.2. you identify any potential hazards relating to your work practices and take the necessary corrective action	Speak to communicate information, ideas and opinions adapting speech and content to take account of the listener(s) medium.	Speaking and Listening Level 1		
3.3. you carry out your work practices to comply with the given instructions to maintain safe and healthy working conditions	Read and obtain information of varying length and detail from different sources. Listen and respond to spoken language, including information and narratives, and follow explanations and instructions of varying length, adapting response to speaker, medium and context.	Reading Level 2 Speaking and Listening Level 1		

Getting the basics right in Construction (Common Occupations)

Unit MR 138: Maintain and use woodworking hand tools

Element 1: Select resources

National Standard of Work	Literacy National Standard	Level Title	Numeracy National Standard	Level Title
1.1. you confirm that you understand your instructions	Read and understand straightforward texts of varying length on a variety of topics accurately and independently. Listen and respond to spoken language, including information and narratives, and follow explanations and instructions of varying length, adapting response to speaker, medium and context.	Reading Level 1 Speaking and Listening Level 1		
1.2. you ensure the selected quantity and quality of the resources are in accordance with the given instructions and, where they are unsuitable, take the necessary corrective action by reporting to the person in charge	Read and obtain information from different sources. Speak to communicate information, ideas and opinions adapting speech and content to take account of the listener(s) medium. Listen and respond to spoken language, including information and narratives, and follow explanations and instructions of varying length, adapting response to speaker, medium and context.	Reading Level 1 Speaking and Listening Level 1	Generate results to a given level of accuracy using methods, measures and checking procedures appropriate to the specified purpose – use whole numbers – use common measures.	Calculating and manipulating mathematical information Level 1

Unit MR 138: Maintain and use woodworking hand tools

Element 2: Work materials using hand tools

National Standard of Work	Literacy National Standard	Level Title	Numeracy National Standard	Level Title
2.1. you carry out your work practices to comply with the given instructions and you achieve the required quality of finish to your work	Read and obtain information from different sources. Listen and respond to spoken language, including information and narratives, and follow explanations and instructions of varying length, adapting response to speaker, medium and context.	Reading Level 1 Speaking and Listening Level 1		
2.2. you put right any deficiencies in the quality of your work by corrective action in accordance with the given instructions	Read and obtain information from different sources. Listen and respond to spoken language, including information and narratives, and follow explanations and instructions of varying length, adapting response to speaker, medium and context.	Reading Level 1 Speaking and Listening Level 1		
2.3. you carry out your work practices to comply with the given instructions to minimise the risk of damage to the resources and surrounding work area	Read and obtain information from different sources. Listen and respond to spoken language, including information and narratives, and follow explanations and instructions of varying length, adapting response to speaker, medium and context.	Reading Level 1 Speaking and Listening Level 1		
2.4. you comply with the given instructions when carrying out your work practices to maintain safe working procedures	Read and obtain information of varying length and detail from different sources. Listen and respond to spoken language, including information and narratives, and follow explanations and instructions of varying length, adapting response to speaker, medium and context.	Reading Level 2 Speaking and Listening Level 1		

Unit MR 138: Maintain and use woodworking hand tools

Element 3: Comply with safe working practices

National Standard of Work	Literacy National Standard	Level Title	Numeracy National Standard	Level Title
3.1. you carry out your work practices to keep areas clean, free from debris and waste in accordance with the given instructions	Read and obtain information from different sources. Listen and respond to spoken language, including information and narratives, and follow explanations and instructions of varying length, adapting response to speaker, medium and context.	Reading Level 1 Speaking and Listening Level 1		
3.2. you identify any potential hazards relating to your work practices and take the necessary corrective action	Speak to communicate information, ideas and opinions adapting speech and content to take account of the listener(s) medium.	Speaking and Listening Level 1		
3.3. you carry out your work practices to comply with the given instructions to maintain safe and healthy working conditions	Read and obtain information of varying length and detail from different sources. Listen and respond to spoken language, including information and narratives, and follow explanations and instructions of varying length, adapting response to speaker, medium and context.	Reading Level 2 Speaking and Listening Level 1		

Unit MR 139: Form basic woodworking joints

Element 1: Select resources

National Standard of Work	Literacy National Standard	Level Title	Numeracy National Standard	Level Title
1.1. you confirm that you understand your instructions	Read and understand straightforward texts of varying length on a variety of topics accurately and independently. Listen and respond to spoken language, including information and narratives, and follow explanations and instructions of varying length, adapting response to speaker, medium and context.	Reading Level 1 Speaking and Listening Level 1		
1.2. you ensure the selected quantity and quality of the resources are in accordance with the given instructions and, where they are unsuitable, take the necessary corrective action by reporting to the person in charge	Read and obtain information from different sources. Speak to communicate information, ideas and opinions adapting speech and content to take account of the listener(s) medium. Listen and respond to spoken language, including information and narratives, and follow explanations and instructions of varying length, adapting response to speaker, medium and context.	Reading Level 1 Speaking and Listening Level 1 Speaking and Listening Level 1	Generate results to a given level of accuracy using methods, measures and checking procedures appropriate to the specified purpose – use whole numbers – use common measures.	Calculating and manipulating mathematical information Level 1

Unit MR 139: Form basic woodworking joints

Element 2: Mark out and form joints

National Standard of Work	Literacy National Standard	Level Title	Numeracy National Standard	Level Title
2.1. you carry out your work practices to comply with the given instructions and you achieve the required quality of finish to your work	Read and obtain information from different sources. Listen and respond to spoken language, including information and narratives, and follow explanations and instructions of varying length, adapting response to speaker, medium and context.	Reading Level 1 Speaking and Listening Level 1	Read and understand straightforward mathematical information used for different purposes and independently select relevant information from given graphical, numerical and written material.	Understanding and using mathematical information Level 1
2.2. you put right any deficiencies in the quality of your work by corrective action in accordance with the given instructions	Read and obtain information from different sources. Listen and respond to spoken language, including information and narratives, and follow explanations and instructions of varying length, adapting response to speaker, medium and context.	Reading Level 1 Speaking and Listening Level 1	Generate results to a given level of accuracy using methods, measures and checking procedures appropriate to the specified purpose – use common measures.	Calculating and manipulating mathematical information Level 1
2.3. you carry out your work practices to comply with the given instructions to minimise the risk of damage to the work and surrounding work area	Read and obtain information from different sources. Listen and respond to spoken language, including information and narratives, and follow explanations and instructions of varying length, adapting response to speaker, medium and context.	Reading Level 1 Speaking and Listening Level 1		
2.4. you comply with the given instructions when carrying out your work practices to maintain safe working procedures	Read and obtain information of varying length and detail from different sources. Listen and respond to spoken language, including information and narratives, and follow explanations and instructions of varying length, adapting response to speaker, medium and context.	Reading Level 2 Speaking and Listening Level 1		

Unit MR 139: Form basic woodworking joints

Element 3: Comply with safe working practices

National Standard of Work	Literacy National Standard	Level Title	Numeracy National Standard	Level Title
3.1. you carry out your work practices to keep areas clean, free from debris and waste in accordance with the given instructions	Read and obtain information from different sources. Listen and respond to spoken language, including information and narratives, and follow explanations and instructions of varying length, adapting response to speaker, medium and context.	Reading Level 1 Speaking and Listening Level 1		
3.2. you identify any potential hazards relating to your work practices and take the necessary corrective action	Speak to communicate information, ideas and opinions adapting speech and content to take account of the listener(s) medium.	Speaking and Listening Level 1		
3.3. you carry out your work practices to comply with the given instructions to maintain safe and healthy working conditions	Read and obtain information of varying length and detail from different sources. Listen and respond to spoken language, including information and narratives, and follow explanations and instructions of varying length, adapting response to speaker, medium and context.	Reading Level 2 Speaking and Listening Level 1		

Unit MR 140: Install components hung on hinges

Element 1: Select resources

National Standard of Work	Literacy National Standard	Level Title	Numeracy National Standard	Level Title
1.1. you confirm that you understand your instructions	Read and understand straightforward texts of varying length on a variety of topics accurately and independently. Listen and respond to spoken language, including information and narratives, and follow explanations and instructions of varying length, adapting response to speaker, medium and context.	Reading Level 1 Speaking and Listening Level 1		
1.2. you ensure the selected quantity and quality of the resources are in accordance with the given instructions and, where they are unsuitable, take the necessary corrective action by reporting to the person in charge	Read and obtain information from different sources. Speak to communicate information, ideas and opinions adapting speech and content to take account of the listener(s) medium. Listen and respond to spoken language, including information and narratives, and follow explanations and instructions of varying length, adapting response to speaker, medium and context.	Reading Level 1 Speaking and Listening Level 1 Speaking and Listening Level 1	Generate results to a given level of accuracy using methods, measures and checking procedures appropriate to the specified purpose – use whole numbers – use common measures.	Calculating and manipulating mathematical information Level 1

Unit MR 140: Install components hung on hinges

Element 2: Hang hinged components

National Standard of Work	Literacy National Standard	Level Title	Numeracy National Standard	Level Title
2.1. you carry out your work practices to comply with the given instructions and you achieve the required quality of finish to your work	Read and obtain information from different sources. Listen and respond to spoken language, including information and narratives, and follow explanations and instructions of varying length, adapting response to speaker, medium and context.	Reading Level 1 Speaking and Listening Level 1		
2.2. you put right any deficiencies in the quality of your work by corrective action in accordance with the given instructions	Read and obtain information from different sources. Listen and respond to spoken language, including information and narratives, and follow explanations and instructions of varying length, adapting response to speaker, medium and context.	Reading Level 1 Speaking and Listening Level 1		
2.3. you carry out your work practices to comply with the given instructions to minimise the risk of damage to the work and surrounding work area	Read and obtain information from different sources. Listen and respond to spoken language, including information and narratives, and follow explanations and instructions of varying length, adapting response to speaker, medium and context.	Reading Level 1 Speaking and Listening Level 1		
2.4. you comply with the given instructions when carrying out your work practices to maintain safe working procedures	Read and obtain information of varying length and detail from different sources. Listen and respond to spoken language, including information and narratives, and follow explanations and instructions of varying length, adapting response to speaker, medium and context.	Reading Level 2 Speaking and Listening Level 1		

Getting the basics right in Construction (Common Occupations)

Unit MR 140: Install components hung on hinges

Element 3: Comply with safe working practices

National Standard of Work	Literacy National Standard	Level Title	Numeracy National Standard	Level Title
3.1. you carry out your work practices to keep areas clean, free from debris and waste in accordance with the given instructions	Read and obtain information from different sources. Listen and respond to spoken language, including information and narratives, and follow explanations and instructions of varying length, adapting response to speaker, medium and context.	Reading Level 1 Speaking and Listening Level 1		
3.2. you identify any potential hazards relating to your work practices and take the necessary corrective action	Speak to communicate information, ideas and opinions adapting speech and content to take account of the listener(s) medium.	Speaking and Listening Level 1		
3.3. you carry out your work practices to comply with the given instructions to maintain safe and healthy working conditions	Read and obtain information of varying length and detail from different sources. Listen and respond to spoken language, including information and narratives, and follow explanations and instructions of varying length, adapting response to speaker, medium and context.	Reading Level 2 Speaking and Listening Level 1		

Unit MR 141: Install door ironmongery components

Element 1: Select resources

National Standard of Work	Literacy National Standard	Level Title	Numeracy National Standard	Level Title
1.1. you confirm that you understand your instructions	Read and understand straightforward texts of varying length on a variety of topics accurately and independently. Listen and respond to spoken language, including information and narratives, and follow explanations and instructions of varying length, adapting response to speaker, medium and context.	Reading Level 1 Speaking and Listening Level 1		
1.2. you ensure the selected quantity and quality of the resources are in accordance with the given instructions and, where they are unsuitable, take the necessary corrective action by reporting to the person in charge	Read and obtain information from different sources. Speak to communicate information, ideas and opinions adapting speech and content to take account of the listener(s) medium. Listen and respond to spoken language, including information and narratives, and follow explanations and instructions of varying length, adapting response to speaker, medium and context.	Reading Level 1 Speaking and Listening Level 1 Speaking and Listening Level 1	Generate results to a given level of accuracy using methods, measures and checking procedures appropriate to the specified purpose – use whole numbers – use common measures.	Calculating and manipulating mathematical information Level 1

Getting the basics right in Construction (Common Occupations)

Unit MR 141: Install door ironmongery components

Element 2: Fit ironmongery

National Standard of Work	Literacy National Standard	Level Title	Numeracy National Standard	Level Title
2.1. you carry out your work practices to comply with the given instructions and you achieve the required quality of finish to your work	Read and obtain information from different sources. Listen and respond to spoken language, including information and narratives, and follow explanations and instructions of varying length, adapting response to speaker, medium and context.	Reading Level 1 Speaking and Listening Level 1	Read and understand straightforward mathematical information used for different purposes and independently select relevant information from given graphical, numerical and written material.	Understanding and using mathematical information Level 1
2.2. you put right any deficiencies in the quality of your work by corrective action In accordance with the given instructions	Speak to communicate information, ideas and opinions adapting speech and content to take account of the listener(s) medium.	Speaking and Listening Level 1	Read and understand straightforward mathematical information used for different purposes and independently select relevant information from given graphical, numerical and written material.	Understanding and using mathematical information Level 1
2.3. you carry out your work practices to comply with the given instructions to minimise the risk of damage to the work and surrounding work area	Read and obtain information of varying length and detail from different sources. Listen and respond to spoken language, including information and narratives, and follow explanations and instructions of varying length, adapting response to speaker, medium and context.	Reading Level 2 Speaking and Listening Level 1		
2.4. you comply with the given instructions when carrying out your work practices to maintain safe working procedures	Read and obtain information of varying length and detail from different sources. Listen and respond to spoken language, including information and narratives, and follow explanations and instructions of varying length, adapting response to speaker, medium and context.	Reading Level 2 Speaking and Listening Level 1		

Unit MR 141: Install door ironmongery components

Element 3: Comply with safe working practices

National Standard of Work	Literacy National Standard	Level Title	Numeracy National Standard	Level Title
3.1. you carry out your work practices to keep areas clean, free from debris and waste in accordance with the given instructions	Read and obtain information from different sources. Listen and respond to spoken language, including information and narratives, and follow explanations and instructions of varying length, adapting response to speaker, medium and context.	Reading Level 1 Speaking and Listening Level 1		
3.2. you identify any potential hazards relating to your work practices and take the necessary corrective action	Speak to communicate information, ideas and opinions adapting speech and content to take account of the listener(s) medium.	Speaking and Listening Level 1		
3.3. you carry out your work practices to comply with the given instructions to maintain safe and healthy working conditions	Read and obtain information of varying length and detail from different sources. Listen and respond to spoken language, including information and narratives, and follow explanations and instructions of varying length, adapting response to speaker, medium and context.	Reading Level 2 Speaking and Listening Level 1		

Unit MR 142: Install internal mouldings

Element 1: Select resources

National Standard of Work	Literacy National Standard	Level Title	Numeracy National Standard	Level Title
1.1. you confirm that you understand your instructions	Read and understand straightforward texts of varying length on a variety of topics accurately and independently. Listen and respond to spoken language, including information and narratives, and follow explanations and instructions of varying length, adapting response to speaker, medium and context.	Reading Level 1 Speaking and Listening Level 1		
1.2. you ensure the selected quantity and quality of the resources are in accordance with the given instructions and, where they are unsuitable, take the necessary corrective action by reporting to the person in charge	Read and obtain information from different sources. Speak to communicate information, ideas and opinions adapting speech and content to take account of the listener(s) medium. Listen and respond to spoken language, including information and narratives, and follow explanations and instructions of varying length, adapting response to speaker, medium and context.	Reading Level 1 Speaking and Listening Level 1 Speaking and Listening Level 1	Generate results to a given level of accuracy using methods, measures and checking procedures appropriate to the specified purpose. – use whole numbers – use common measures	Calculating and manipulating mathematical information Level 1

Unit MR 142: Install internal mouldings

Element 2: Position and secure mouldings

National Standard of Work	Literacy National Standard	Level Title	Numeracy National Standard	Level Title
2.1. you carry out your work practices to comply with the given instructions and you achieve the required quality of finish to your work	Read and obtain information from different sources. Listen and respond to spoken language, including information and narratives, and follow explanations and instructions of varying length, adapting response to speaker, medium and context.	Reading Level 1 Speaking and Listening Level 1		
2.2. you put right any deficiencies in the quality of your work by corrective action in accordance with the given instructions	Read and obtain information from different sources. Listen and respond to spoken language, including information and narratives, and follow explanations and instructions of varying length, adapting response to speaker, medium and context.	Reading Level 1 Speaking and Listening Level 1		
2.3. you carry out your work practices to comply with the given instructions to minimise the risk of damage to the work and surrounding work area	Read and obtain information from different sources. Listen and respond to spoken language, including information and narratives, and follow explanations and instructions of varying length, adapting response to speaker, medium and context.	Reading Level 1 Speaking and Listening Level 1		
2.4. you comply with the given instructions when carrying out your work practices to maintain safe working procedures	Read and obtain information of varying length and detail from different sources. Listen and respond to spoken language, including information and narratives, and follow explanations and instructions of varying length, adapting response to speaker, medium and context.	Reading Level 2 Speaking and Listening Level 1		

Getting the basics right in Construction (Common Occupations)

Unit MR 142: Install internal mouldings

Element 3: Comply with safe working practices

National Standard of Work	Literacy National Standard	Level Title	Numeracy National Standard	Level Title
3.1. you carry out your work practices to keep areas clean, free from debris and waste in accordance with the given instructions	Read and obtain information from different sources. Listen and respond to spoken language, including information and narratives, and follow explanations and instructions of varying length, adapting response to speaker, medium and context.	Reading Level 1 Speaking and Listening Level 1		
3.2. you identify any potential hazards relating to your work practices and take the necessary corrective action	Speak to communicate information, ideas and opinions adapting speech and content to take account of the listener(s) medium.	Speaking and Listening Level 1		
3.3. you carry out your work practices to comply with the given instructions to maintain safe and healthy working conditions	Read and obtain information of varying length and detail from different sources. Listen and respond to spoken language, including information and narratives, and follow explanations and instructions of varying length, adapting response to speaker, medium and context.	Reading Level 2 Speaking and Listening Level 1		

Getting the basics right in Construction (Common Occupations)

Basic Skills Maps – Plastering

detailed maps of the Performance Criteria in each Element

Unit MR 01: Load and Unload resources

Element 1: Select resources

National Standard of Work	Literacy National Standard	Level Title	Numeracy National Standard	Level Title
1.1 you confirm that you understand your instructions	Read and understand straightforward texts of varying length on a variety of topics accurately and independently. Listen and respond to spoken language, including information and narratives, and follow explanations and instructions of varying length, adapting response to speaker, medium and context.	Reading Level 1 Speaking and Listening Level 1		
1.2 you ensure the selected quantity and quality of the resources are in accordance with the given instructions and, where they are unsuitable, take the necessary corrective action by report to the person in charge	Read and obtain information from different sources. Speak to communicate information, ideas and opinions adapting speech and content to take account of the listener(s) medium. Listen and respond to spoken language, including information and narratives, and follow explanations and instructions of varying length, adapting response to speaker, medium and context.	Reading Level 1 Speaking and Listening Level 1	Generate results to a given level of accuracy using methods, measures and checking procedures appropriate to the specified purpose – use whole numbers – use common measures.	Calculating and manipulating mathematical information Level 1

Unit MR 01: Load and unload resources

Element 2: Move resources manually

National Standard of Work	Literacy National Standard	Level Title	Numeracy National Standard	Level Title
2.1 you carry out your work practices to comply with the given instructions and you achieve the required movement of resources	Read and obtain information from different sources. Listen and respond to spoken language, including information and narratives, and follow explanations and instructions of varying length, adapting response to speaker, medium and context.	Reading Level 1 Speaking and Listening Level 1		
2.2 you put right any deficiencies in the stacking and positioning of resources by corrective action in accordance with the given instructions	Read and obtain information from different sources. Listen and respond to spoken language, including information and narratives, and follow explanations and instructions of varying length, adapting response to speaker, medium and context.	Reading Level 1 Speaking and Listening Level 1		
2.3 you carry out your work practices to comply with the given instructions to minimise the risk of damage to the resources and surrounding work area	Read and obtain information from different sources. Listen and respond to spoken language, including information and narratives, and follow explanations and instructions of varying length, adapting response to speaker, medium and context.	Reading Level 1 Speaking and Listening Level 1		
2.4 you comply with the given instructions when carrying out your work practices to maintain safe working procedures	Read and obtain information from different sources. Listen and respond to spoken language, including information and narratives, and follow explanations and instructions of varying length, adapting response to speaker, medium and context.	Reading Level 2 Speaking and Listening Level 1		

Unit MR 01: Load and unload resources

Element 3: Comply with safe working practices

National Standard of Work	Literacy National Standard	Level Title	Numeracy National Standard	Level Title
3.1 you carry out your work practices to keep areas clean, free from debris and waste in accordance with the given instructions	Read and obtain information from different sources. Listen and respond to spoken language, including information and narratives, and follow explanations and instructions of varying length, adapting response to speaker, medium and context.	Reading Level 1 Speaking and Listening Level 1		
3.2 you identify any potential hazards relating to your work practices and take the necessary corrective action	Speak to communicate information, ideas and opinions adapting speech and content to take account of the listener(s) medium.	Speaking and Listening Level 1		
3.3 you carry out your work practices to comply with the given instructions to maintain safe and healthy working conditions	Read and obtain information of varying length and detail from different sources. Listen and respond to spoken language, including information and narratives, and follow explanations and instructions of varying length, adapting response to speaker, medium and context.	Reading Level 2 Speaking and Listening Level 1		

Getting the basics right in Construction (Common Occupations)

Unit MR 02: Contribute to erecting and dismantling working platforms

Element 1: Select resources

National Standard of Work	Literacy National Standard	Level Title	Numeracy National Standard	Level Title
1.1 you confirm that you understand your instructions	Read and understand straightforward texts of varying length on a variety of topics accurately and independently. Listen and respond to spoken language, including information and narratives, and follow explanations and instructions of varying length, adapting response to speaker, medium and context.	Reading Level 1 Speaking and Listening Level 1		
1.2 you ensure the selected quantify and quality of the resources are in accordance with the given instructions and, where they are unsuitable, take the necessary corrective action by reporting to the person in charge	Read and obtain information from different sources. Speak to communicate information, ideas and opinions adapting speech and content to take account of the listener(s) medium. Listen and respond to spoken language, including information and narratives, and follow explanations and instructions of varying length, adapting response to speaker, medium and context.	Reading Level 1 Speaking and Listening Level 1	Generate results to a given level of accuracy using methods, measures and checking procedures appropriate to the specified purpose – use whole numbers – use common measures.	Calculating and manipulating mathematical information Level 1

Unit MR 02: Contribute to erecting and dismantling working platforms

Element 2: Assist with erecting and dismantling access equipment

National Standard of Work	Literacy National Standard	Level Title	Numeracy National Standard	Level Title
2.1 you carry out your work practices to comply with the given instructions and you achieve a safe working platform	Read and obtain information from different sources. Listen and respond to spoken language, including information and narratives, and follow explanations and instructions of varying length, adapting response to speaker, medium and context.	Reading Level 1 Speaking and Listening Level 1		
2.2 you put right any deficiencies in the quality of your work by corrective action in accordance with the given instructions	Read and obtain information from different sources. Listen and respond to spoken language, including information and narratives, and follow explanations and instructions of varying length, adapting response to speaker, medium and context.	Reading Level 1 Speaking and Listening Level 1		
2.3 you carry out your work practices to comply with the given instructions to minimise the risk of damage to the work and surrounding work area	Read and obtain information from different sources. Listen and respond to spoken language, including information and narratives, and follow explanations and instructions of varying length, adapting response to speaker, medium and context.	Reading Level 1 Speaking and Listening Level 1		
2.4 you comply with the given instructions when carrying out your work practices to maintain safe working procedures	Read and obtain information from different sources. Listen and respond to spoken language, including information and narratives, and follow explanations and instructions of varying length, adapting response to speaker, medium and context.	Reading Level 2 Speaking and Listening Level 1		

Getting the basics right in Construction (Common Occupations)

Unit MR 02: Contribute to erecting and dismantling working platforms

Element 3: Comply with safe working practices

National Standard of Work	Literacy National Standard	Level Title	Numeracy National Standard	Level Title
3.1 you carry out your work practices to keep areas clean, free from debris and waste in accordance with the given instructions	Read and obtain information from different sources. Listen and respond to spoken language, including information and narratives, and follow explanations and instructions of varying length, adapting response to speaker, medium and context.	Reading Level 1 Speaking and Listening Level 1		
3.2 you identify any potential hazards relating to your work practices and take the necessary corrective action	Speak to communicate information, ideas and opinions adapting speech and content to take account of the listener(s) medium.	Speaking and Listening Level 1		
3.3 you carry out your work practices to comply with the given instructions to maintain safe and healthy working conditions	Read and obtain information from different sources. Listen and respond to spoken language, including information and narratives, and follow explanations and instructions of varying length, adapting response to speaker, medium and context.	Reading Level 2 Speaking and Listening Level 1		

Unit MR 03: Contribute to maintaining work relationships

Element 1: Identify potential areas of conflict

National Standard of Work	Literacy National Standard	Level Title	Numeracy National Standard	Level Title
1.1 conflicts resulting from work practices relating to your colleagues are resolved by corrective action	Engage in discussion with one or more people in a variety of different situations, making clear and effective contributions that produce outcomes appropriate to purpose and topic.	Speaking and Listening Level 2		
1.2 areas of potential conflicts are identified and dealt with by corrective action before problems arise	Engage in discussion with one or more people in a variety of different situations, making clear and effective contributions that produce outcomes appropriate to purpose and topic.	Speaking and Listening Level 2		
1.3 you carry out your work practices to avoid causing conflicts with your colleagues	Engage in discussion with one or more people in a variety of different situations, making clear and effective contributions that produce outcomes appropriate to purpose and topic.	Speaking and Listening Level 2		

Getting the basics right in Construction (Common Occupations)

Unit MR 03: Contribute to maintaining work relationships

Element 2: Maintain relationships with colleagues

National Standard of Work	Literacy National Standard	Level Title	Numeracy National Standard	Level Title
2.1 your relationships with colleagues are maintained during work practices to achieve the required productivity	Engage in discussion with one or more people in familiar and unfamiliar situations, making clear and relevant contributions that respond to what others say and produce a shared understanding about different topics.	Speaking and Listening Level 2		
2.2 time is taken to establish and maintain constructive relationships with your colleagues	Speak to communicate information, ideas and opinions adapting speech and content to take account of the listener(s) medium.	Speaking and Listening Level 2		
2.3 you carry out your work practices to take account of views and opinions of your colleagues	Listen and respond to spoken language, including extended information and narratives, and follow detailed explanations and multi-step instructions of varying length, adapting response to speaker, medium and context.	Speaking and Listening Level 2		

Unit MR 214: Prepare and mix materials

Element 1: Select resources

National Standard of Work	Literacy National Standard	Level Title	Numeracy National Standard	Level Title
1.1 you confirm that you understand your instructions	Read and understand straightforward texts of varying length on a variety of topics accurately and independently.	Reading Level 1		
	Listen and respond to spoken language, including information and narratives, and follow explanations and instructions of varying length, adapting response to speaker, medium and context.	Speaking and Listening Level 1		
1.2 you ensure the selected quantity and quality of the resources are in accordance with the given instructions and, where they are unsuitable, take the necessary corrective action by report to the person in charge	Read and obtain information from different sources.	Reading Level 1	Generate results to a given level of accuracy using methods, measures and checking procedures appropriate to the specified purpose – use whole numbers – use common measures.	Calculating and manipulating mathematical information Level 1
	Speak to communicate information, ideas and opinions adapting speech and content to take account of the listener(s) medium.	Speaking and Listening Level 2		
	Listen and respond to spoken language, including information and narratives, and follow explanations and instructions of varying length, adapting response to speaker, medium and context.	Speaking and Listening Level 2		

Unit MR 214: Prepare and mix materials

Element 2: Prepare and mix materials

National Standard of Work	Literacy National Standard	Level Title	Numeracy National Standard	Level Title
2.1 you carry out your work practices to comply with the given instructions and you achieve the required mix specification	Read and obtain information from different sources. Listen and respond to spoken language, including information and narratives, and follow explanations and instructions of varying length, adapting response to speaker, medium and context.	Reading Level 1 Speaking and Listening Level 1	Read and understand straightforward mathematical information used for different purposes and independently select relevant information from given graphical, numerical and written material.	Understanding and using mathematical information Level 1
2.2 you put right any deficiencies in the quality of your work by corrective action In accordance wlth the glven instructions	Read and obtain information from different sources. Listen and respond to spoken language, including information and narratives, and follow explanations and instructions of varying length, adapting response to speaker, medium and context.	Reading Level 1 Speaking and Listening Level 1	Generate results to a given level of accuracy using methods, measures and checking procedures appropriate to the specified purpose – use common measures.	Calculating and manipulating mathematical information Level 1
2.3 you carry out your work practices to comply with the given instructions to minimise the risk of damage to the work and surrounding work area	Read and obtain information from different sources. Listen and respond to spoken language, including information and narratives, and follow explanations and instructions of varying length, adapting response to speaker, medium and context.	Reading Level 1 Speaking and Listening Level 1		
2.4 you comply with the given instructions when carrying out your work practices to maintain safe working procedures	Read and obtain information from different sources. Listen and respond to spoken language, including information and narratives, and follow explanations and instructions of varying length, adapting response to speaker, medium and context.	Reading Level 2 Speaking and Listening Level 1		

Unit MR 214: Prepare and mix materials

Element 3: Comply with safe working practices

National Standard of Work	Literacy National Standard	Level Title	Numeracy National Standard	Level Title
3.1 you carry out your work practices to keep areas clean, free from debris and waste in accordance with the given instructions	Read and obtain information from different sources. Listen and respond to spoken language, including information and narratives, and follow explanations and instructions of varying length, adapting response to speaker, medium and context.	Reading Level 1 Speaking and Listening Level 1		
3.2 you identify any potential hazards relating to your work practices and take the necessary corrective action	Speak to communicate information, ideas and opinions adapting speech and content to take account of the listener(s) medium.	Speaking and Listening Level 1		
3.3 you carry out your work practices to comply with the given instructions to maintain safe and healthy working conditions	Read and obtain information of varying length and detail from different sources. Listen and respond to spoken language, including information and narratives, and follow explanations and instructions of varying length, adapting response to speaker, medium and context.	Reading Level 2 Speaking and Listening Level 1		

Getting the basics right in Construction (Common Occupations)

Unit MR 215: Prepare background surfaces

Element 1: Select resources

National Standard of Work	Literacy National Standard	Level Title	Numeracy National Standard	Level Title
1.1 you confirm that you understand your instructions	Read and understand straightforward texts of varying length on a variety of topics accurately and independently. Listen and respond to spoken language, including information and narratives, and follow explanations and instructions of varying length, adapting response to speaker, medium and context.	Reading Level 1 Speaking and Listening Level 1		
1.2 you ensure the selected quantity and quality of the resources are in accordance with the given instructions and, where they are unsuitable, take the necessary corrective action by reporting to the person in charge	Read and obtain information from different sources. Speak to communicate information, ideas and opinions adapting speech and content to take account of the listener(s) medium. Listen and respond to spoken language, including information and narratives, and follow explanations and instructions of varying length, adapting response to speaker, medium and context.	Reading Level 1 Speaking and Listening Level 1 Speaking and Listening Level 1	Generate results to a given level of accuracy using methods, measures and checking procedures appropriate to the specified purpose – use whole numbers – use common measures.	Calculating and manipulating mathematical information Level 1

Unit MR 215: Prepare background surfaces

Element 2: Prepare background surfaces

National Standard of Work	Literacy National Standard	Level Title	Numeracy National Standard	Level Title
2.1 you carry out your work practices to comply with the given instructions and you achieve the required background specification	Read and obtain information from different sources. Listen and respond to spoken language, including information and narratives, and follow explanations and instructions of varying length, adapting response to speaker, medium and context.	Reading Level 1 Speaking and Listening Level 1		
2.2 you put right any deficiencies in the quality of your work by corrective action in accordance with the given instructions	Read and obtain information from different sources. Listen and respond to spoken language, including information and narratives, and follow explanations and instructions of varying length, adapting response to speaker, medium and context.	Reading Level 1 Speaking and Listening Level 1		
2.3 you carry out your work practices to comply with the given instructions to minimise the risk of damage to the work and surrounding work area	Read and obtain information from different sources. Listen and respond to spoken language, including information and narratives, and follow explanations and instructions of varying length, adapting response to speaker, medium and context.	Reading Level 1 Speaking and Listening Level 1		
2.4 you comply with the given instructions when carrying out your work practices to maintain safe working procedures	Read and obtain information of varying length and detail from different sources. Listen and respond to spoken language, including information and narratives, and follow explanations and instructions of varying length, adapting response to speaker, medium and context.	Reading Level 2 Speaking and Listening Level 1		

Getting the basics right in Construction (Common Occupations)

Unit MR 215: Prepare background surfaces

Element 3: Comply with safe working practices

National Standard of Work	Literacy National Standard	Level Title	Numeracy National Standard	Level Title
3.1 you carry out your work practices to keep areas clean, free from debris and waste in accordance with the given instructions	Read and obtain information from different sources. Listen and respond to spoken language, including information and narratives, and follow explanations and instructions of varying length, adapting response to speaker, medium and context.	Reading Level 1 Speaking and Listening Level 1		
3.2 you identify any potential hazards relating to your work practices and take the necessary corrective action	Speak to communicate information, ideas and opinions adapting speech and content to take account of the listener(s) medium.	Speaking and Listening Level 1		
3.3 you carry out your work practices to comply with the given instructions to maintain safe and healthy working conditions	Read and obtain information of varying length and detail from different sources. Listen and respond to spoken language, including information and narratives, and follow explanations and instructions of varying length, adapting response to speaker, medium and context.	Reading Level 2 Speaking and Listening Level 1		

Unit MR 216: Cut components to a dimension

Element 1: Select resources for cutting

National Standard of Work	Literacy National Standard	Level Title	Numeracy National Standard	Level Title
1.1 you confirm that you understand your instructions	Read and understand straightforward texts of varying length on a variety of topics accurately and independently. Listen and respond to spoken language, including information and narratives, and follow explanations and instructions of varying length, adapting response to speaker, medium and context.	Reading Level 1 Speaking and Listening Level 1	Read and understand straightforward mathematical information used for different purposes and independently select relevant information from given graphical, numerical and written material.	Understanding and using mathematical information Level 1
1.2 you ensure the selected quantity and quality of the resources are in accordance with the given instructions and, where they are unsuitable, take the necessary corrective action by report to the person in charge	Read and obtain information from different sources. Speak to communicate information, ideas and opinions adapting speech and content to take account of the listener(s) medium. Listen and respond to spoken language, including information and narratives, and follow explanations and instructions of varying length, adapting response to speaker, medium and context.	Reading Level 1 Speaking and Listening Level 1 Speaking and Listening Level 1	Generate results to a given level of accuracy using methods, measures and checking procedures appropriate to the specified purpose – use whole numbers – use common measures.	Calculating and manipulating mathematical information Level 1

Getting the basics right in Construction (Common Occupations)

Unit MR 216: Cut components to a dimension

Element 2: Cut components to size

National Standard of Work	Literacy National Standard	Level Title	Numeracy National Standard	Level Title
2.1 you carry out your work practices to comply with the given instructions and you achieve the required specification for cutting	Read and obtain information from different sources. Listen and respond to spoken language, including information and narratives, and follow explanations and instructions of varying length, adapting response to speaker, medium and context.	Reading Level 1 Speaking and Listening Level 1	Generate results to a given level of accuracy using methods, measures and checking procedures appropriate to the specified purpose – use common measures.	Calculating and manipulating mathematical information Level 1
2.2 you put right any deficiencies in the quality of your work by corrective action in accordance with the given instructions	Read and obtain information from different sources. Listen and respond to spoken language, including information and narratives, and follow explanations and instructions of varying length, adapting response to speaker, medium and context.	Reading Level 1 Speaking and Listening Level 1	Generate results to a given level of accuracy using methods, measures and checking procedures appropriate to the specified purpose – use common measures.	Calculating and manipulating mathematical information Level 1
2.3 you carry out your work practices to comply with the given instructions to minimise the risk of damage to the work and surrounding work area	Read and obtain information from different sources. Listen and respond to spoken language, including information and narratives, and follow explanations and instructions of varying length, adapting response to speaker, medium and context.	Reading Level 1 Speaking and Listening Level 1		
2.4 you comply with the given instructions when carrying out your work practices to maintain safe working procedures	Read and obtain information of varying length and detail from different sources. Listen and respond to spoken language, including information and narratives, and follow explanations and instructions of varying length, adapting response to speaker, medium and context.	Reading Level 2 Speaking and Listening Level 1		

Unit MR 216: Cut components to a dimension

Element 3: Comply with safe working practices

National Standard of Work	Literacy National Standard	Level Title	Numeracy National Standard	Level Title
3.1 you carry out your work practices to keep areas clean, free from debris and waste in accordance with the given instructions	Read and obtain information from different sources. Listen and respond to spoken language, including information and narratives, and follow explanations and instructions of varying length, adapting response to speaker, medium and context.	Reading Level 1 Speaking and Listening Level 1		
3.2 you identify any potential hazards relating to your work practices and take the necessary corrective action	Speak to communicate information, ideas and opinions adapting speech and content to take account of the listener(s) medium.	Speaking and Listening Level 1		
3.3 you carry out your work practices to comply with the given instructions to maintain safe and healthy working conditions	Read and obtain information of varying length and detail from different sources. Listen and respond to spoken language, including information and narratives, and follow explanations and instructions of varying length, adapting response to speaker, medium and context.	Reading Level 1 Speaking and Listening Level 1		

Unit MR 217: Contribute to producing plastering components

Element 1: Select materials and components

National Standard of Work	Literacy National Standard	Level Title	Numeracy National Standard	Level Title
1.1 moving and storing of materials and components is carried out safely to instruction and the work requirements	Read and understand straightforward texts of varying length on a variety of topics accurately and independently. Listen and respond to spoken language, including information and narratives, and follow explanations and instructions of varying length, adapting response to speaker, medium and context.	Reading Level 1 Speaking and Listening Level 1		
1.2 you ensure the selected quantity and quality of the resources are in accordance with the given instructions and, where they are unsuitable, take the necessary corrective action by reporting to the person in charge	Read and obtain information from different sources. Speak to communicate information, ideas and opinions adapting speech and content to take account of the listener(s) medium. Listen and respond to spoken language, including information and narratives, and follow explanations and instructions of varying length, adapting response to speaker, medium and context.	Reading Level 1 Speaking and Listening Level 1 Speaking and Listening Level 1	Generate results to a given level of accuracy using methods, measures and checking procedures appropriate to the specified purpose – use whole numbers – use common measures.	Calculating and manipulating mathematical information Level 1

Unit MR 217: Contribute to producing plastering components

Element 2: Contribute to producing plastering components

National Standard of Work	Literacy National Standard	Level Title	Numeracy National Standard	Level Title
2.1 you carry out your work practices to comply with the given instructions and you achieve the required quality of finish to your work	Read and obtain information from different sources. Listen and respond to spoken language, including information and narratives, and follow explanations and instructions of varying length, adapting response to speaker, medium and context.	Reading Level 1 Speaking and Listening Level 1	Generate results to a given level of accuracy using methods, measures and checking procedures appropriate to the specified purpose – use whole numbers – use common measures.	Calculating and manipulating mathematical information Level 1
2.2 you put right any deficiencies in the quality of your work by corrective action in accordance with the given instructions	Read and obtain information from different sources. Listen and respond to spoken language, including information and narratives, and follow explanations and instructions of varying length, adapting response to speaker, medium and context.	Reading Level 1 Speaking and Listening Level 1		
2.3 you carry out your work practices to comply with the given instructions to minimise the risk of damage to the work and surrounding work area	Read and obtain information from different sources. Listen and respond to spoken language, including information and narratives, and follow explanations and instructions of varying length, adapting response to speaker, medium and context.	Reading Level 1 Speaking and Listening Level 1		
2.4 you comply with the given instructions when carrying out your work practices to maintain safe working procedures	Read and obtain information of varying length and detail from different sources. Listen and respond to spoken language, including information and narratives, and follow explanations and instructions of varying length, adapting response to speaker, medium and context.	Reading Level 2 Speaking and Listening Level 1		

Getting the basics right in Construction (Common Occupations)

Unit MR 217: Contribute to producing plastering components

Element 3: Comply with safe working practices

National Standard of Work	Literacy National Standard	Level Title	Numeracy National Standard	Level Title
3.1 you carry out your work practices to keep areas clean, free from debris and waste in accordance with the given instructions	Read and obtain information from different sources. Listen and respond to spoken language, including information and narratives, and follow explanations and instructions of varying length, adapting response to speaker, medium and context.	Reading Level 1 Speaking and Listening Level 1		
3.2 you identify any potential hazards relating to your work practices and take the necessary corrective action	Speak to communicate information, ideas and opinions adapting speech and content to take account of the listener(s) medium.	Speaking and Listening Level 1		
3.3 you carry out your work practices to comply with the given instructions to maintain safe and healthy working conditions	Read and obtain information of varying length and detail from different sources. Listen and respond to spoken language, including information and narratives, and follow explanations and instructions of varying length, adapting response to speaker, medium and context.	Reading Level 2 Speaking and Listening Level 1		

Unit MR 218: Apply materials to backgrounds

Element 1: Select resources for use

National Standard of Work	Literacy National Standard	Level Title	Numeracy National Standard	Level Title
1.1 you confirm that you understand your instructions	Read and understand straightforward texts of varying length on a variety of topics accurately and independently. Listen and respond to spoken language, including information and narratives, and follow explanations and instructions of varying length, adapting response to speaker, medium and context.	Reading Level 1 Speaking and Listening Level 1		
1.2 you ensure the selected quantity and quality of the resources are in accordance with the given instructions and, where they are unsuitable, take the necessary corrective action by reporting to the person in charge	Read and obtain information from different sources. Speak to communicate information, ideas and opinions adapting speech and content to take account of the listener(s) medium. Listen and respond to spoken language, including information and narratives, and follow explanations and instructions of varying length, adapting response to speaker, medium and context.	Reading Level 1 Speaking and Listening Level 1 Speaking and Listening Level 1	Generate results to a given level of accuracy using methods, measures and checking procedures appropriate to the specified purpose – use whole numbers – use common measures.	Calculating and manipulating mathematical information Level 1

Unit MR 218: Apply materials to backgrounds

Element 2: Prepare for and apply materials to surfaces

National Standard of Work	Literacy National Standard	Level Title	Numeracy National Standard	Level Title
2.1 you carry out your work practices to comply with the given instructions and you achieve the required quality of finish to your work	Read and obtain information from different sources. Listen and respond to spoken language, including information and narratives, and follow explanations and instructions of varying length, adapting response to speaker, medium and context.	Reading Level 1 Speaking and Listening Level 1		
2.2 you put right any deficiencies in the quality of your work by corrective action in accordance with the given instructions	Read and obtain information from different sources. Listen and respond to spoken language, including information and narratives, and follow explanations and instructions of varying length, adapting response to speaker, medium and context.	Reading Level 1 Speaking and Listening Level 1		
2.3 you carry out your work practices to comply with the given instructions to minimise the risk of damage to the work and surrounding work area	Read and obtain information from different sources. Listen and respond to spoken language, including information and narratives, and follow explanations and instructions of varying length, adapting response to speaker, medium and context.	Reading Level 1 Speaking and Listening Level 1		
2.4 you comply with the given instructions when carrying out your work practices to maintain safe working procedures	Read and obtain information of varying length and detail from different sources. Listen and respond to spoken language, including information and narratives, and follow explanations and instructions of varying length, adapting response to speaker, medium and context.	Reading Level 2 Speaking and Listening Level 1		

Unit MR 218: Apply materials to backgrounds

Element 3: Comply with safe working practices

National Standard of Work	Literacy National Standard	Level Title	Numeracy National Standard	Level Title
3.1 you carry out your work practices to keep areas clean, free from debris and waste in accordance with the given instructions	Read and obtain information from different sources. Listen and respond to spoken language, including information and narratives, and follow explanations and instructions of varying length, adapting response to speaker, medium and context.	Reading Level 1 Speaking and Listening Level 1		
3.2 you identify any potential hazards relating to your work practices and take the necessary corrective action	Speak to communicate information, ideas and opinions adapting speech and content to take account of the listener(s) medium.	Speaking and Listening Level 1		
3.3 you carry out your work practices to comply with the given instructions to maintain safe and healthy working conditions	Read and obtain information of varying length and detail from different sources. Listen and respond to spoken language, including information and narratives, and follow explanations and instructions of varying length, adapting response to speaker, medium and context.	Reading Level 2 Speaking and Listening Level 1		

Getting the basics right in Construction (Common Occupations)

7. Progression from the Adult Literacy Standards to the Adult Literacy Core Curriculum

National Standards for Adult Literacy

The progression between capabilities

Entry Level		

ENTRY 1 LEVEL	ENTRY 2 LEVEL	ENTRY 3 LEVEL
Speaking and listening *At this level, adults can*	**Speaking and listening** *At this level, adults can*	**Speaking and listening** *At this level, adults can*
listen and respond to spoken language, including simple narratives, statements, questions and single-step instructions	**listen and respond** to spoken language, including straightforward information, short narratives, explanations and instructions	**listen and respond** to spoken language, including straightforward information and narratives, and follow straightforward explanations and instructions, both face to face and on the telephone
speak to communicate basic information, feelings and opinions on familiar topics	**speak to communicate** information, feelings and opinions on familiar topics	**speak to communicate** information, feelings and opinions on familiar topics, using appropriate formality, both face to face and on the telephone
engage in discussion with another person in a familiar situation about familiar topics	**engage in discussion** with one or more people in a familiar situation to establish shared understanding about familiar topics	**engage in discussion** with one or more people in a familiar situation, making relevant points and responding to what others say to reach a shared understanding about familiar topics
Reading *At this level, adults can*	**Reading** *At this level, adults can*	**Reading** *At this level, adults can*
read and understand short texts with repeated language patterns on familiar topics	**read and understand** short, straightforward texts on familiar topics	**read and understand** short, straightforward texts on familiar topics accurately and independently
read and obtain information from common signs and symbols	**read and obtain information** from short documents, familiar sources and signs and symbols	**read and obtain information** from everyday sources
Writing *At this level, adults can*	**Writing** *At this level, adults can*	**Writing** *At this level, adults can*
write to communicate information to an intended audience	**write to communicate** information with some awareness of the intended audience	**write to communicate** information and opinions with some adaptation to the intended audience

Getting the basics right in Construction (Common Occupations)

LEVEL 1	**LEVEL 2**
Speaking and listening *At this level, adults can*	***Speaking and listening*** *At this level, adults can*
listen and respond to spoken language, including information and narratives, and follow explanations and instructions of varying lengths, adapting response to speaker, medium and context	**listen and respond** to spoken language, including extended information and narratives, and follow detailed explanations and multi-step instructions of varying length, adapting response to speaker, medium and context
speak to communicate information, ideas and opinions adapting speech and content to take account of the listener(s) and medium	**speak to communicate** straightforward and detailed information, ideas and opinions clearly, adapting speech and content to take account of the listener(s), medium, purpose and situation
engage in discussion with one or more people In familiar and unfamiliar situations, making clear and relevant contributions that respond to what others say and produce a shared understanding about different topics	**engage in discussion** with one or more people in a variety of different situations, making clear and effective contributions that produce outcomes appropriate to purpose and topic
Reading *At this level, adults can*	***Reading*** *At this level, adults can*
read and understand straightforward texts of varying length on a variety of topics accurately and independently	**read and understand** a range of texts of varying complexity accurately and independently
read and obtain information from different sources	**read and obtain information** of varying length and detail from different sources
Writing *At this level, adults can*	***Writing*** *At this level, adults can*
write to communicate information, ideas and opinions clearly using length, format and style appropriate to purpose and audience	**write to communicate** information, ideas and opinions clearly and effectively, using length, format and style appropriate to purpose, content and audience

Speaking and listening: the progression between curriculum elements

	Entry Level	

TEXT FOCUS	**ENTRY 1 LEVEL**	**ENTRY 2 LEVEL**
Listen and respond	**SLlr/E1.1** Listen for the gist of short explanations **SLlr/E1.2** Listen for detail using key words to extract some specific information **SLlr/E1.3** Follow single-step instructions in a familiar context, asking for instructions to be repeated if necessary **SLlr/E1.4** Listen and respond to requests for personal information	**SLlr/E2.1** Listen for and follow the gist of explanations, instructions and narratives **SLlr/E2.2** Listen for detail in short explanations, instructions and narratives **SLlr/E2.3** Listen for and identify the main points of short explanations or presentations **SLlr/E2.4** Listen to and follow short, straightforward explanations and instructions **SLlr/E2.5** Listen to and identify simply expressed feelings and opinions **SLlr/E2.6** Respond to straightforward questions
Speak to communicate	**SLc/E1.1** Speak clearly to be heard and understood in simple exchanges **SLc/E1.2** Make requests using appropriate terms **SLc/E1.3** Ask questions to obtain specific information **SLc/E1.4** Make statements of fact clearly	**SLc/E2.1** Speak clearly to be heard and understood in straightforward exchanges **SLc/E2.2** Make requests and ask questions to obtain information in everyday contexts **SLc/E2.3** Express clearly statements of fact, and short accounts and descriptions **SLc/E2.4** Ask questions to clarify understanding
Engage in discussion	**SLd/E1.1** Speak and listen in simple exchanges and everyday contexts	**SLd/E2.1** Follow the gist of discussions **SLd/E2.2** Follow the main points and make appropriate contributions to the discussion

Getting the basics right in Construction (Common Occupations)

Entry Level 3	Level 1	Level 2
SLlr/E3.1 Listen for and follow the gist of explanations, instructions and narratives in different contexts **SLlr/E3.2** Listen for detail in explanations, instructions and narratives in different contexts **SLlr/E3.3** Listen for and identify relevant information and new information from discussions, explanations and presentations **SLlr/E3.4** Use strategies to clarify and confirm understanding (e.g. facial expressions or gestures) **SLlr/E3.5** Listen to and respond appropriately to other points of view **SLlr/E3.6** Respond to a range of questions about familiar topics	**SLlr/L1.1** Listen for and identify relevant information from explanations and presentations on a range of straightforward topics **SLlr/L1.2** Listen for and understand explanations, instructions and narratives on different topics in a range of contexts **SLlr/L1.3** Use strategies to clarify and confirm understanding (e.g. facial expressions, body language and verbal prompts) **SLlr/L1.4** Provide feedback and confirmation when listening to others **SLlr/L1.5** Make contributions relevant to the situation and the subject **SLlr/L1.6** Respond to questions on a range of topics	**SLlr/L2.1** Listen for and identify relevant information from extended explanations or presentations on a range of topics **SLlr/L2.2** Listen to, understand and follow lengthy or multi-step instructions and narratives on a range of topics and in a range of contexts **SLlr/L2.3** Respond to detailed or extended questions on a range of topics **SLlr/L2.4** Respond to criticism and criticise constructively
SLc/E3.1 Speak clearly to be heard and understood using appropriate clarity, speed and phrasing **SLc/E3.2** Use formal language and register when appropriate **SLc/E3.3** Express clearly statements of fact and give short explanations, accounts and descriptions **SLc/E3.4** Make requests and ask questions to obtain information in familiar and unfamiliar contexts	**SLc/L1.1** Speak clearly in a way which suits the situation **SLc/L1.2** Make requests and ask questions to obtain information in familiar and unfamiliar contexts **SLc/L1.3** Express clearly statements of fact, explanations, instructions, accounts, and descriptions **SLc/L1.4** Present information and ideas in a logical sequence and include detail and develop ideas where appropriate	**SLc/L2.1** Speak clearly and confidently in a way which suits the situation **SLc/L2.2** Make requests and ask questions to obtain detailed information in familiar and unfamiliar contexts **SLc/L2.3** Express clearly statements of fact, explanations, instructions, accounts, descriptions using appropriate structure, style and vocabulary **SLc/L2.4** Present information and ideas in a logical sequence and provide further detail and development to clarify or confirm understanding
SLd/E3.1 Follow and understand the main points of discussions on different topics **SLd/E3.2** Make contributions to discussions that are relevant to the subject **SLd/E3.3** Respect the turn-taking rights of others during discussions	**SLd/L1.1** Follow and contribute to discussions on a range of straightforward topics **SLd/L1.2** Respect the turn-taking rights of others during discussions **SLd/L1.3** Use appropriate phrases for interruption	**SLd/L2.1** Make relevant contributions and help to move discussions forward **SLd/L2.2** Adapt contributions to discussions to suit audience, context, purpose and situation **SLd/L2.3** Use appropriate phrases for interruption and change of topic **SLd/L2.4** Support opinions and arguments with evidence **SLd/L2.5** Use strategies intended to reassure (e.g. body language and appropriate phraseology)

Reading and Writing (Text focus): the progression between curriculum elements

READING ☐   WRITING ▢

	Entry Level	
TEXT FOCUS	**ENTRY 1 LEVEL**	**ENTRY 2 LEVEL**
Reading comprehension	**Rt/E1.1** Follow a short narrative on a familiar topic or experience **Rt/E1.2** Recognise the different purposes of texts at this level	**Rt/E2.1** Trace and understand the main events of chronological and instructional texts **Rt/E2.2** Recognise the different purposes of texts at this level **Rt/E2.3** Identify common sources of information **Rt/E2.4** Use illustrations and captions to locate information
Writing composition	**Wt/E1.1** Use written words and phrases to record or present information	**Wt/E2.1** Use written words and phrases to record or present information

ENTRY LEVEL 3	LEVEL 1	LEVEL 2
Rt/E3.1 Trace and understand the main events of chronological, continuous descriptive and explanatory texts of more than one paragraph **Rt/E3.2** Recognise the different purposes of texts at this level **Rt/E3.3** Recognise and understand the organisational features and typical language of instructional texts (e.g. use of imperatives and second person) **Rt/E3.4** Identify the main points and ideas, and predict words from context **Rt/E3.5** Understand and use organisational features to locate information (e.g. contents, index, menus) **Rt/E3.6** Skim read title, headings and illustrations to decide if material is of interest **Rt/E3.7** Scan texts to locate information **Rt/E3.8** Obtain specific information through detailed reading **Rt/E3.9** Relate an image to print and use it to obtain meaning	**Rt/L1.1** Trace and understand the main events of continuous descriptive, explanatory and persuasive texts **Rt/L1.2** Recognise how language and other textual features are used to achieve different purposes (e.g. to instruct, explain, describe, persuade) **Rt/L1.3** Identify the main points and specific detail, and infer meaning from images which is not explicit in the text **Rt/L1.4** Use organisational and structural features to locate information (e.g. contents, index, menus, subheadings, paragraphs) **Rt/L1.5** Use different reading strategies to find and obtain information	**Rt/L2.1** Trace and understand the main events of continuous descriptive, explanatory and persuasive texts **Rt/L2.2** Identify the purpose of a text and infer meaning which is not explicit **Rt/L2.3** Identify the main points and specific detail **Rt/L2.4** Read an argument and identify the points of view **Rt/L2.5** Read critically to evaluate information, and compare information, ideas and opinions from different sources **Rt/L2.6** Use organisational features and systems to locate texts and information **Rt/L2.7** Use different reading strategies to find and obtain information (e.g. skimming, scanning, detailed reading) **Rt/L2.8** Summarise information from longer documents
Wt/E3.1 Plan and draft writing **Wt/E3.2** Organise writing in short paragraphs **Wt/E3.3** Sequence chronological writing **Wt/E3.4** Proof-read and correct writing for grammar and spelling	**Wt/L1.1** Plan and draft writing **Wt/L1.2** Judge how much to write and the level of detail to include **Wt/L1.3** Present information in a logical sequence using paragraphs where appropriate **Wt/L1.4** Use language suitable for purpose and audience **Wt/L1.5** Use format and structure for different purposes **Wt/L1.6** Proof-read and revise writing for accuracy and meaning	**Wt/L2.1** Plan and draft writing **Wt/L2.2** Judge how much to write and the level of detail to include **Wt/L2.3** Present information and ideas in a logical or persuasive sequence, using paragraphs where appropriate **Wt/L2.4** Use format and structure to organise writing for different purposes **Wt/L2.5** Use formal and informal language appropriate to purpose and audience **Wt/L2.6** Use different styles of writing for different purposes (e.g. persuasive techniques, supporting evidence, technical vocabulary) **Wt/L2.7** Proof-read and revise writing for accuracy and meaning

Reading and Writing (Sentence focus): the progression between curriculum elements

READING ☐   WRITING ▣

Entry Level		

TEXT FOCUS	ENTRY 1 LEVEL	ENTRY 2 LEVEL
Grammar and punctuation	**Rs/E1.1** Read and recognise simple sentence structures	**Rs/E2.1** Read and understand linking words and adverbials in instructions and directions (e.g. *next, then, right* and *straight on*) **Rs/E2.2** Use knowledge of simple sentence structure and word order to help decipher unfamiliar words and predict meaning **Rs/E2.3** Apply own life experience and knowledge to check out plausible meanings of a sentence as a whole when decoding unfamiliar words **Rs/E2.4** Use punctuation and capitalisation to aid understanding
Grammar and punctuation	**Ws/E1.1** Construct a simple sentence **Ws/E1.2** Punctuate a simple sentence with a capital letter and a full stop **Ws/E1.3** Use a capital letter for personal pronoun 'I'	**Ws/E2.1** Construct simple and compound sentences, using common conjunctions to connect two clauses (e.g. *as, and, but*) **Ws/E2.2** Use adjectives **Ws/E2.3** Use punctuation correctly (e.g. capital letters, full stops and question marks) **Ws/E2.4** Use a capital letter for proper nouns

(ENTRY LEVEL 3)	(LEVEL 1)	(LEVEL 2)
Rs/E3.1 Recognise and understand the organisational features and typical language of instructional texts (e.g. use of imperatives, second person) **Rs/E3.2** Use implicit and explicit knowledge of different types of word (e.g. linking words [connectives], nouns, verbs, adjectives), of word order, and of possible plausible meanings, to help decode unfamiliar words and predict meaning **Rs/E3.3** Use punctuation and capitalisation to aid understanding	**Rs/L1.1** Use implicit and explicit grammatical knowledge (e.g. of different sentence forms, types of word, verb tense, word order) along with own knowledge and experience to predict meaning, try out plausible meanings, and to read and check for sense **Rs/L1.2** Use punctuation to help their understanding	**Rs/L2.1** Use implicit and explicit grammatical knowledge, alongside own knowledge and experience of context, to help follow meaning and judge the purpose of different types of text **Rs/L2.2** Use punctuation to help interpret the meaning and purpose of texts
Ws/E3.1 Write in complete sentences **Ws/E3.2** Use correct basic grammar (e.g. appropriate verb tense, subject–verb agreement) **Ws/E3.3** Use punctuation correctly (e.g. capital letters, full stops, question marks, exclamation marks)	**Ws/L1.1** Write in complete sentences **Ws/L1.2** Use correct grammar (e.g. subject–verb agreement, correct use of tense) **Ws/L1.3** Punctuate sentences correctly, and use punctuation so that meaning is clear	**Ws/L2.1** Construct complex sentences **Ws/L2.2** Use correct grammar (e.g. subject – verb agreement, correct and consistent use of tense) **Ws/L2.3** Use pronouns so that their meaning is clear **Ws/L2.4** Punctuate sentences correctly, and use punctuation accurately (e.g. commas, apostrophes, inverted commas)

Reading and Writing (Word focus): the progression between curriculum elements

READING ☐   WRITING ▨

Entry Level		

TEXT FOCUS	ENTRY 1 LEVEL	ENTRY 2 LEVEL
Vocabulary, word recognition and phonics	**Rw/E1.1** Possess a limited, meaningful sight vocabulary of words, signs and symbols **Rw/E1.2** Decode simple, regular words **Rw/E1.3** Recognise the letters of the alphabet in both upper and lower case	**Rw/E2.1** Read and understand words on forms related to personal information (e.g. first name, surname, address, postcode, age, date of birth) **Rw/E2.2** Recognise high-frequency words and words with common spelling patterns **Rw/E2.3** Use phonic and graphic knowledge to decode words **Rw/E2.4** Use a simplified dictionary to find the meaning of unfamiliar words **Rw/E2.5** Use initial letters to find and sequence words in alphabetical order
Spelling and handwriting	**Ww/E1.1** Spell correctly some personal key words and familiar words **Ww/E1.2** Write the letters of the alphabet using upper and lower case **Ww/E1.3** Use basic sound–symbol association to help spelling, *as appropriate for the needs of the learner*	**Ww/E2.1** Spell correctly the majority of personal details and familiar common words **Ww/E2.2** Use their knowledge of sound–symbol relationships and phonological patterns (e.g. consonant clusters and vowel phonemes) to help work out correct spellings, *as appropriate for the needs of the learner* **Ww/E2.3** Produce legible text

ENTRY LEVEL 3	LEVEL 1	LEVEL 2
Rw/E3.1 Recognise and understand relevant specialist key words **Rw/E3.2** Read and understand words and phrases commonly used on forms **Rw/E3.3** Use a dictionary to find the meaning of unfamiliar words **Rw/E3.4** Use first- and second-place letters to find and sequence words in alphabetical order **Rw/E3.5** Use a variety of reading strategies to help decode an increasing range of unfamiliar words	**Rw/L1.1** Use reference material to find the meaning of unfamiliar words **Rw/L1.2** Recognise and understand the vocabulary associated with different types of text, using appropriate strategies to work out meaning **Rw/L1.3** Recognise and understand an increasing range of vocabulary, applying knowledge of word structure, related words, word roots, derivations, borrowings	**Rw/L2.1** Read and understand technical vocabulary **Rw/L2.2** Use reference material to find the meaning of unfamiliar words **Rw/L2.3** Recognise and understand vocabulary associated with texts of different levels of accessibility, formality, complexity and of different purpose
Ww/E3.1 Spell correctly common words and relevant key words for work and special interest **Ww/E3.2** Use their developing knowledge of sound–symbol relationships and phonological patterns to help spell a greater range of words and longer words, *as appropriate for the needs of the learner* **Ww/E3.3** Produce legible text	**Ww/L1.1** Spell correctly words used most often in work, studies and daily life **Ww/L1.2** Produce legible text	**Ww/L2.1** Spell correctly words used most often in work, studies and daily life, including familiar technical words **Ww/L2.2** Produce legible text

Getting the basics right in Construction (Common Occupations)

8. Progression from the Adult Numeracy Standards to the Adult Numeracy Core Curriculum

National Standards for Adult Numeracy

The progression between capabilities

Entry Level		

ENTRY LEVEL 1	**ENTRY LEVEL 2**	**ENTRY LEVEL 3**
Understanding and using mathematical information *At this level, adults can*	*Understanding and using mathematical information* *At this level, adults can*	*Understanding and using mathematical information* *At this level, adults can*
read and understand information given by numbers and symbols in simple graphical, numerical and written material	**read and understand** information given by numbers, symbols, simple diagrams and charts in graphical, numerical and written material	**read and understand** information given by numbers, symbols, diagrams and charts used for different purposes and in different ways in graphical, numerical and written material
specify and describe a practical problem or task using numbers and measures	**specify and describe** a practical problem or task using numbers, measures and simple shapes to record essential information	**specify and describe** a practical problem or task using numbers, measures and diagrams to collect and record relevant information
Calculating and manipulating mathematical information *At this level, adults can*	**Calculating and manipulating mathematical information** *At this level, adults can*	**Calculating and manipulating mathematical information** *At this level, adults can*
generate results which make sense and use given methods and given checking procedures appropriate to the specified purpose	**generate results** to a given level of accuracy using given methods and given checking procedures appropriate to the specified purpose	**generate results** to a given level of accuracy using given methods, measures and checking procedures appropriate to the specified purpose
Interpreting results and communicating mathematical information *At this level, adults can*	*Interpreting results and communicating mathematical information* *At this level, adults can*	*Interpreting results and communicating mathematical information* *At this level, adults can*
present and explain results which show an understanding of the intended purpose using appropriate numbers, measures, objects or pictures	**present and explain results** which meet the intended purpose using appropriate numbers, simple diagrams and symbols	**present and explain results** which meet the intended purpose using appropriate numbers, diagrams, charts and symbols

Understanding and using mathematical information *At this level, adults can*	*Understanding and using mathematical information* *At this level, adults can*
read and understand straightforward mathematical information used for different purposes and independently select relevant information from given graphical, numerical and written material	**read and understand** mathematical information used for different purposes and independently select and compare relevant information from a variety of graphical, numerical and written material
specify and describe a practical activity, problem or task using mathematical information and language to make accurate observations and identify suitable calculations to achieve an appropriate outcome	**specify and describe** a practical activity, problem or task using mathematical information and language to increase understanding and select appropriate methods for carrying through a substantial activity
Calculating and manipulating mathematical information *At this level, adults can*	**Calculating and manipulating mathematical information** *At this level, adults can*
generate results to a given level of accuracy using methods, measures and checking procedures appropriate to the specified purpose	**generate results** to an appropriate level of accuracy using methods, measures and checking procedures appropriate to the specified purpose
Interpreting results and communicating mathematical information *At this level, adults can*	*Interpreting results and communicating mathematical information* *At this level, adults can*
present and explain results which meet the intended purpose using an appropriate format to a given level of accuracy	**present and explain results** clearly and accurately using numerical, graphical and written formats appropriate to purpose, findings and audience

Number: the progression between curriculum elements

	Entry Level	
	ENTRY 1 LEVEL	**ENTRY 2 LEVEL**
Whole numbers	**N1/E1.1** Count reliably up to 10 items **N1/E1.2** Read and write numbers up to 10, including zero **N1/E1.3** Order and compare numbers up to 10, including zero **N1/E1.4** Add single-digit numbers with totals to 10 **N1/E1.5** Subtract single-digit numbers from numbers up to 10 **N1/E1.6** Interpret $+$, $-$ and $=$ in practical situations for solving problems **N1/E1.7** Use a calculator to check calculations using whole numbers	**N1/E2.1** Count reliably up to 20 items **N1/E2.2** Read, write, order and compare numbers up to 100 **N1/E2.3** Add and subtract two-digit whole numbers **N1/E2.4** Recall addition and subtraction facts to 10 **N1/E2.5** Multiply using single-digit whole numbers **N1/E2.6** Approximate by rounding to the nearest 10 **N1/E2.7** Use and interpret $+$, $-$, $\times$ and $\div$ in practical situations for solving problems **N1/E2.8** Use a calculator to check calculations using whole numbers
Fractions, decimals and percentages		**N2/E2.1** Read, write and compare halves and quarters of quantities **N2/E2.2** Find halves and quarters of small numbers of items or shapes

Getting the basics right in Construction (Common Occupations)

ENTRY LEVEL 3	LEVEL 1	LEVEL 2
N1/E3.1 Count, read, write, order and compare numbers up to 1000	**N1/L1.1** Read, write, order and compare numbers, including large numbers	**N1/L2.1** Read, write, order and compare positive and negative numbers of any size in a practical context
N1/E3.2 Add and subtract using three-digit whole numbers	**N1/L1.2** Recognise negative numbers in practical contexts (e.g. temperatures)	**N1/L2.2** Carry out calculations with numbers of any size using efficient methods
N1/E3.3 Recall addition and subtraction facts to 20	**N1/L1.3** Add, subtract, multiply and divide using efficient written methods	**N1/L2.3** Calculate ratio and direct proportion
N1/E3.4 Multiply two-digit whole numbers by single-digit whole numbers	**N1/L1.4** Multiply and divide whole numbers by 10 and 100	**N1/L2.4** Evaluate expressions and make substitutions in given formulae in words and symbols to produce results
N1/E3.5 Recall multiplication facts (e.g. multiples of 2, 3, 4, 5, 10)	**N1/L1.5** Recall multiplication facts up to 10×10 and make connections with division facts	
N1/E3.6 Divide two-digit whole numbers by single-digit whole numbers and interpret remainders	**N1/L1.6** Recognise numerical relationships (e.g. multiples and squares)	
N1/E3.7 Approximate by rounding numbers less than 1000 to the nearest 10 or 100	**N1/L1.7** Work out simple ratio and direct proportion	
N1/E3.8 Estimate answers to calculations	**N1/L1.8** Approximate by rounding	
N1/E3.9 Use and interpret $+$, $-$, $\times$, $\div$ and $=$ in practical situations for solving problems	**N1/L1.9** Estimate answers to calculations	
N2/E3.1 Read, write and understand common fractions (e.g. $\frac{3}{4}$, $\frac{2}{3}$, $\frac{1}{10}$)	**N2/L1.1** Read, write, order and compare common fractions and mixed numbers	**N2/L2.1** Use fractions to order and compare amounts or quantities
N2/E3.2 Recognise and use equivalent forms (e.g. $\frac{5}{10} = \frac{1}{2}$)	**N2/L1.2** Find parts of whole number quantities or measurements (e.g. $\frac{2}{3}$ or $\frac{3}{4}$)	**N2/L2.2** Identify equivalencies between fractions, decimals and percentages
N2/E3.3 Read, write and understand decimals up to two decimal places in practical contexts (such as: common measures to one decimal place, e.g. 1.5 m; money in decimal notation, e.g. £2.37)	**N2/L1.3** Recognise equivalencies between common fractions, percentages and decimals (e.g. 50% $= \frac{1}{2}$, 0.25 $= \frac{1}{4}$) and use these to find part of whole-number quantities	**N2/L2.3** Evaluate one number as a fraction of another
N2/E3.4 Use a calculator to calculate using whole numbers and decimals to solve problems in context, and to check calculations	**N2/L1.4** Read, write, order and compare decimals up to three decimal places	**N2/L2.4** Use fractions to add and subtract amounts or quantities
	N2/L1.5 Add, subtract, multiply and divide decimals up to two places	**N2/L2.5** Order, approximate and compare decimals when solving practical problems
	N2/L1.6 Multiply and divide decimals by 10, 100	**N2/L2.6** Add, subtract, multiply and divide decimals up to three places
	N2/L1.7 Approximate decimals by rounding to a whole number or two decimal places	**N2/L2.7** Order and compare percentages and understand percentage increase and decrease
	N2/L1.8 Read, write, order and compare simple percentages, and understand simple percentage increase and decrease	**N2/L2.8** Find percentage parts of quantities and measurements
	N2/L1.9 Find simple percentage parts of quantities and measurements	**N2/L2.9** Evaluate one number as a percentage of another
	N2/L1.10 Find simple percentage increase and decrease	**N2/L2.10** Use a calculator to calculate efficiently using whole numbers, fractions, decimals and percentages
	N2/L1.11 Use a calculator to calculate efficiently using whole numbers, fractions, decimals and percentages	

Measures, shape and space: the progression between curriculum elements

	Entry Level	
	ENTRY LEVEL 1	**ENTRY LEVEL 2**
Common measures	**MSS1/E1.1** Recognise and select coins and notes	**MSS1/E2.1** Make amounts of money up to £1 in different ways using 1p, 2p, 5p, 10p, 20p and 50p coins
	MSS1/E1.2 Relate familiar events to: times of the day; days of the week; seasons of the year	**MSS1/E2.2** Calculate the cost of more than one item and the change from a transaction, in pence or in whole pounds
	MSS1/E1.3 Describe size and use direct comparisons for the size of at least two items	**MSS1/E2.3** Read and record time in common date formats
	MSS1/E1.4 Describe length, width, height, and use direct comparisons for length, width and height of items	**MSS1/E2.4** Read and understand time displayed on analogue and 12-hour digital clocks in hours, half hours and quarter hours
	MSS1/E1.5 Describe weight and use direct comparisons for the weight of items	**MSS1/E2.5** Read, estimate, measure and compare length using common standard and non-standard units (e.g. metre, centimetre, paces)
	MSS1/E1.6 Describe capacity and use direct comparisons for the capacity of items	**MSS1/E2.6** Read, estimate, measure and compare weight using common standard units (e.g. kilogram)
		MSS1/E2.7 Read, estimate, measure and compare capacity using common standard and non-standard units (e.g. litre, cupful)
		MSS1/E2.8 Read and compare positive temperatures in everyday situations such as weather charts
		MSS1/E2.9 Read simple scales to the nearest labelled division
Shape and space	**MSS2/E1.1** Recognise and name common 2-D and 3-D shapes	**MSS2/E2.1** Recognise and name 2-D and 3-D shapes
	MSS2/E1.2 Understand everyday positional vocabulary (e.g. between, inside or near to)	**MSS2/E2.2** Describe the properties of common 2-D and 3-D shapes
		MSS2/E2.3 Use positional vocabulary

Entry Level 3	Level 1	Level 2
MSS1/E3.1 Add and subtract sums of money using decimal notation **MSS1/E3.2** Round sums of money to the nearest £ and 10p and make approximate calculations **MSS1/E3.3** Read, measure and record time **MSS1/E3.4** Read and interpret distance in everyday situations **MSS1/E3.5** Read, estimate, measure and compare length using non-standard and standard units **MSS1/E3.6** Read, estimate, measure and compare weight using non-standard and standard units **MSS1/E3.7** Read, estimate, measure and compare capacity using non-standard and standard units **MSS1/E3.8** Choose and use appropriate units and measuring instruments **MSS1/E3.9** Read, measure and compare temperature using common units and instruments	**MSS1/L1.1** Add, subtract, multiply and divide sums of money and record **MSS1/L1.2** Read, measure and record time in common date formats and in the 12-hour and 24-hour clock **MSS1/L1.3** Calculate using time **MSS1/L1.4** Read, estimate, measure and compare length, weight, capacity and temperature using common units and instruments **MSS1/L1.5** Read, estimate, measure and compare distance **MSS1/L1.6** Add and subtract common units of measure within the same system **MSS1/L1.7** Convert units of measure in the same system **MSS1/L1.8** Work out the perimeter of simple shapes **MSS1/L1.9** Work out the area of rectangles **MSS1/L1.10** Work out simple volume (e.g. cuboids)	**MSS1/L2.1** Calculate with sums of money and convert between currencies **MSS1/L2.2** Calculate, measure and record time in different formats **MSS1/L2.3** Estimate, measure and compare length, distance, weight and capacity using metric and, where appropriate, imperial units **MSS1/L2.4** Estimate, measure and compare temperature, including reading scales and conversion tables **MSS1/L2.5** Calculate with units of measure within the same system **MSS1/L2.6** Calculate with units of measure between systems, using conversion tables and scales, and approximate conversion factors **MSS1/L2.7** Understand and use given formulae for finding perimeters and areas of regular shapes (e.g. rectangular and circular surfaces) **MSS1/L2.8** Understand and use given formulae for finding areas of composite shapes (e.g. non-rectangular rooms or plots of land) **MSS1/L2.9** Understand and use given formulae for finding volumes of regular shapes (e.g. a cuboid or cylinder) **MSS1/L2.10** Work out dimensions from scale drawings (e.g. 1:20)
MSS2/E3.1 Sort 2-D and 3-D shapes to solve practical problems using properties (e.g. lines of symmetry, side length, angles)	**MSS2/L1.1** Solve problems using the mathematical properties of regular 2-D shapes (e.g. tessellation or symmetry) **MSS2/L1.2** Draw 2-D shapes in different orientations using grids (e.g. in diagrams or plans)	**MSS2/L2.1** Recognise and use common 2-D representations of 3-D objects (e.g. in maps and plans) **MSS2/L2.2** Solve problems involving 2-D shapes and parallel lines (e.g. in laying down carpet tiles)

Handling data: the progression between curriculum elements

	Entry Level	
	ENTRY 1 LEVEL	ENTRY 2 LEVEL
Data and statistical measures	**HD1/E1.1** Extract simple information from lists **HD1/E1.2** Sort and classify objects using a single criterion **HD1/E1.3** Construct simple representations or diagrams, using knowledge of numbers, measures or shape and space	**HD1/E2.1** Extract information from lists, tables, simple diagrams and block graphs **HD1/E2.2** Make numerical comparisons from block graphs **HD1/E2.3** Sort and classify objects using two criteria **HD1/E2.4** Collect simple numerical information **HD1/E2.5** Represent information so that it makes sense to others (e.g. in lists, tables and diagrams)
Probability		

ENTRY 3 LEVEL	LEVEL 1	LEVEL 2
HD1/E3.1 Extract numerical information from lists, tables, diagrams and simple charts **HD1/E3.2** Make numerical comparisons from bar charts and pictograms **HD1/E3.3** Make observations and record numerical information using a tally **HD1/E3.4** Organise and represent information in different ways so that it makes sense to others	**HD1/L1.1** Extract and interpret information (e.g. in tables, diagrams, charts and line graphs) **HD1/L1.2** Collect, organise and represent discrete data (e.g. in tables, charts, diagrams and line graphs) **HD1/L1.3** Find the arithmetical average (mean) for a set of data **HD1/L1.4** Find the range for a set of data	**HD1/L2.1** Extract discrete and continuous data from tables, diagrams, charts and line graphs **HD1/L2.2** Collect, organise and represent discrete and continuous data in tables, charts, diagrams and line graphs **HD1/L2.3** Find the mean, median and mode, and use them as appropriate to compare two sets of data **HD1/L2.4** Find the range and use it to describe the spread within sets of data
	HD2/L1.1 Show that some events are more likely to occur than others **HD2/L1.2** Express the likelihood of an event using fractions, decimals and percentages with the probability scale of 0 to 1	**HD2/L2.1** Identify the range of possible outcomes of combined events and record the information using diagrams or tables

9. Information and contacts

For information about basic skills, the Basic Skills National Standards, the Adult Literacy Core Curriculum and the Adult Numeracy Core Curriculum contact:

The Basic Skills Agency
Commonwealth House,
1-19 New Oxford Street, London WC1A 1NU
Tel: 020 7405 4017
Fax: 020 7440 6626
Website: **www.basic-skills.co.uk**

For information about the national strategy contact:

Adult Literacy and Numeracy Strategy Unit
Department for Education and Skills
Caxton House – Level 1G
Tothill Street
London SW1H 9NF
andrew.graham@dfee.gov.uk
Website: **www.dfee.gov.uk/readwriteplus**

For leaflets, research documents and publications related to basic skills, contact:

Basic Skills Agency Orderline
Admail 524, London WC1A 1BR
Tel: 0870 600 2400 Fax: 0870 600 2401

For information about signposting to National Training Organisations, contact:

NTO National Council
10 Meadowcourt, Amos Road, Sheffield S9 1BX
Tel: 0114 261 9926
Email: **London@nto-nc.org**

Useful publications include:

Adult Literacy Core Curriculum, The Basic Skills Agency, 2001

Adult Numeracy Core Curriculum, The Basic Skills Agency, 2001

Basic Skills are Union Business, The Basic Skills Agency, 2000

Public Sector, Public Potential, The Basic Skills Agency, 2000

Improving literacy and numeracy – A fresh start, The Basic Skills Agency, 1999